Prana

Master the Art of Pranayama Breathing

(Breathing Techniques to Calm Your Mind Relieve Stress and Heal Your Body)

William Ward

Published By **Darby Connor**

William Ward

*Pranayama: Master the Art of Pranayama
Breathing (Breathing Techniques to Calm Your
Mind Relieve Stress and Heal Your Body)*

ISBN   978-1-7780652-3-1

No part of this guidebook shall be reproduced in any form without permission in writing from the publisher except in the case of brief quotations embodied in critical articles or reviews.

Legal & Disclaimer

The information contained in this book is not designed to replace or take the place of any form of medicine or professional medical advice. The information in this book has been provided for educational & entertainment purposes only.

The information contained in this book has been compiled from sources deemed reliable, and it is accurate to the best of the Author's knowledge; however, the Author cannot guarantee its accuracy and validity and cannot be held liable for any errors or omissions. Changes are periodically made to this book. You must consult your doctor or get professional medical advice before using any of the suggested remedies, techniques, or information in this book.

Table Of Contents

Chapter 1: Pranayama Breathing

Most humans fee their mobile telephones after they visit bed each night time time, however how can we recharge our minds? The terrific and handiest way may additionally definitely be in your respiration.

Pranayama comes from a Sanskrit word that describes yoga breathing sporting activities that can enhance bodily fitness, highbrow readability, release strain, and growth power. The word "breathwork" is a brand new term this is used to offer an reason for pranayama or breathing sports.

Yoga is an historic Indian machine that proclaims prana as being the strength or conventional existence stress that distinguishes the dead from the residing. This energy or existence strain flows through strength channels called Nadi and the chakra's strength facilities.

Prana is a critical power that we want in our subtle and bodily layers, and if we don't have it, we will die. Prana is what maintains us dwelling.

Prana has severa meaning stages, from recognition strength to our physical breath to our innovative strength given starting to kundalini shakti. Yogis will inform you that the complete universe became constructed from prana.

Prana is a chunk tough to understand thinking about that we are able to't see it. But we're capable of sense it. Having a smooth recognition of what prana is and isn't, you could be so associated that you could enjoy the prana. Once we're capable to connect with prana, we are able to hook up with the arena and who we really are.

Even despite the fact that prana pertains to the breath, it isn't our actual breath. It's an strength that travels at some level inside the frame via a community of channels. You should study it to the imperative concerned machine. All of those channels connect everything within the mind and body and behave like a conduit for prana.

There are over 3000 years that reference to prana that has transcended non secular traditions and cultures. Prana has been a number one a part of tantric yoga, hatha yoga, ayurvedic, and Hindu traditions, but all of them speak to the "existence pressure." The Hebrew's ruah, the Islamic's ruh, the pneuma of historic Greeks, the anima or ancient Romans, and the Chinese chi may be seen in the Christian's Holy Spirit.

Even no matter the fact that it can no longer be similar to respiration, prana can be described as breathing or breath. More definitions encompass soul, spirit, internal winds, vital winds, spiritual power, or lifestyles stress.

Some traditions have positioned among five and ten severa prana types that relate to downward, upward, outward, and inward shifting strength or power that relates to particular locations within the frame just like the digestion, heart, throat, or head.

Every human has a frame. We additionally have an energetic body and a physical form. Our active body is every so often referred to as the diffused body. It is what a few humans talk with as an air of mystery because it extends further than our our bodies. You've heard the pronouncing, "they moderate up a room." This is wherein that pronouncing comes from. It is how we sense any other character's electricity.

This subtle frame has a precious worried device crafted from nadis or channels made up of one tremendous channel, and side channels, which some visit due to the reality the moon and solar, and 72,000 smaller channels. Depending at the manner of life, there might be greater than 72,000 channels.

The solar channel, or Pingala, travels up the right of the spine. It is represented thru "ha" in Sanskrit. This is a crimson channel wherein ignorant disliking, aversions, separateness, jealousy, and anger want to stay. All in their "warmness" energies had been associated with the solar.

As this electricity travels through the Pingala channel on the exhale, we want to enjoy rejection. Ignorant disliking may be categorised like this due to the reality we suppose that doing away with unique subjects or people from our lives will supply us happiness. But a smart individual is aware about that happiness pleasant comes from internal us.

The moon channel, or ida, runs up the left of the backbone. It is represented by way of "tha" in Sanskrit. All the cooler energies go together with the waft through this channel like ignorant liking, attachment, cravings, and desires.

When prana moves upward at the same time as we inhale, our mind gets drawn to any item that we preference. It "ignorantly" craves what it thinks will make us happy. A sensible man or woman is aware about that happiness comes from inner, and happiness as a way to closing isn't observed in humans or gadgets.

Found proper in front of the backbone is the avadhuti, Sushumna, shaking channel, growing a track channel, or critical channel. Its call refers back to the hum we feel even as we feel real bliss that comes upi while prana can freely float thru the Nadi.

The final intention of the "ha-tha" yoga is to transport the "ha" and "tha" energies out of the factor channels and into the principle channel. "Hatha" yoga modified into to start with practiced to pull and push the inner breath into the treasured channel by using manipulating the bodily frame.

If prana freely flows on this essential channel, we've got reached Samadhi, that's considered complete integration. This is characterised through the use of emotions of contentment, herbal joy, and understanding.

These channels wrap spherical and art work collectively in various important elements all through the frame. These are referred to as "wheels," and we understand them as chakras. These charkas bypass the critical channel ought to change into choke factors and will block prana movement. When you pay interest that a person has a blocked chakra, this vital channel has been gummed up through some aspect inside one of the chakras.

The precise huge variety and vicinity of the chakras range in every culture. Most Hindu traditions say there are both seven or six chakras, while Buddhists say there are 5.

Meditation and yoga can unblock the ones factors via transferring a number of the prana moving in the aspect channels into that vital channel. When you're physically doing yoga, you can experience an electric powered rate because it's far going thru your frame. Anytime you get a "gut feeling" or "a shiver," you are responding for your 6th feel.

You can also want to appearance what prana is doing with the beneficial resource of genuinely looking your breath. When prana's energy movements through the right channel, it will exit via your proper nose. During this time, the left, logical part of the thoughts will become activated. If you spark off the left nose, the proper and innovative a part of the mind is greater dominant.

Usually, there can be most effective one aspect of the nose that is greater dominant than the possibility, which changes every hour. If you've got got reached a kingdom of whole absorption, samadhi, or nirvana even as you meditate, you may be able to breathe similarly out each nostrils simultaneously. You don't have strength flowing via the facet channels.

One of the pleasant techniques to connect to the prana is to be aware wonderful sensations you sense while you breathe. It isn't an twist of future that we relate our inhale to colorful feelings, awake emotions, more energy, and happiness. When we exhale our breath, we are respiration out disappointments, disappointment, and letting circulate of the horrific things in lifestyles. The cycle of unhappiness and happiness, impermanent and constantly converting, is a cycle that we live interior whilst we're respiratory.

When yoga pulls, pushes, and actions the internal breath inside the course of the critical channel with the useful resource of bodily manipulating the body, meditation does the equal issue through influencing the mind. Ancient texts will say that someone's mind right their prana like a person rides a horse. Because of this, you can manual your prana using your thoughts and go with the flow them to the center channel.

By pranayama and meditation, we're capable of learn how to control our breath. Most human beings have noticed while meditation receives interrupted, and our respiration does too. If our meditation is resting and calm, we acquired't be able to word our breath.

Because breath and thoughts are connected, they may be capable of change via specializing in clearly one. One of the yoga limbs is controlling your breath with the beneficial aid of the usage of sports activities activities to manipulate your prana via the usage of asana and meditation. Properly used pranayama techniques can remedy ailments and keep us healthy. There are many tremendous techniques on hand that could help us boom our power, calm and easy our minds, and warm the frame. One take a look at completed in 2012 indicates that doing the ujjayi approach can flip off our pressure response.

By combining pranayama, meditation, and asana, your Kundalini electricity mendacity dormant at the bottom of your backbone will begin to journey upward through that critical channel. It will then be launched through the crown chakra, bringing your enlightenment. For a few, this can handiest take area as fast as they die even as our prana receives sent to the coronary coronary heart chakra and then launch through the crown.

Since prana is a ordinary strength that just doesn't exist inner us, we aren't separated from the fireplace's, water's, earth's, and wind's power sooner or later of the complete worldwide. Our inner breath is associated with the breath out of doors.

While we exercising being aware about the prana in our breath and body, we may additionally moreover need to exercise noticing how energy moves inside the global spherical us and impacts the surroundings and weather and the way the intoxicants, caffeine, and food we devour affect our strength.

Being privy to prana and our diffused frame takes us an entire lifestyles. During meditation, being aware of thoughts offers the right situations to respond as it should be. Being privy to the gives that prana gives us is the same capability. With time and growing a better hobby, we are capable of intentionally go with the flow electricity in the direction of the primary channel and experience contentment and bliss which could by no means be disturbed.

There are severa resources to maintain, keep, and growth the volume of your prana. You may want to classify the ones into 4 important instructions: calmness, breath, relaxation, and food.

You will discover greater prana in sparkling food that you could in stale or canned meals. The ingredients that vegetarians consume are better in prana, but because of the reality meat is lifeless, it's far taken into consideration terrible or pretty low prana.

The notable deliver of prana is your breath. If your respiration stops, you can die. As I will circulate over in a few minutes, how we breathe can profoundly have an effect on the way we revel in.

It emerge as determined that the extremely good and amount of prana and the manner it flows thru the strength channels can determine our u . S . Of thoughts.

Because we don't pay sufficient interest to our strength channels, they might turn out to be a chunk blocked, making the flowing prana jerky or broken. This need to result in having bad feelings, doubts, depression, anxiety, battle, uncertainty, worry, and fear.

If our prana levels are excessive and can glide in a regular, easy, and non-stop motion, our minds can be enthusiastic, high-quality, happy, and calm.

The historical yoga scriptures component out and description numerous pranayama strategies.

The Patanjali Yoga Sutra 2.Forty nine gives pranayama the definition of: "In that usa of being in asana or posture, breaking the identical vintage motion of inhalation or exhalation is law of breath."

This manner that prana is the standard life strain and that Ayama works to increase or alter it.

These historic yogis determined how effective the breath became, and it is able to boom a person's prana. So they created a completely unique respiratory approach that modified into capable of growth a person's energy, create calmness, preserve health, and easy their mind in order that they'll meditate higher.

Pranayama isn't a way to control your respiratory, as some human beings assume, but it allows you manipulate your prana or strength together with your breath. Those strategies incorporate respiratory via your nostrils in a pattern wherein you can inhale, preserve your breath, and exhale. Some of the most commonplace breathing wearing events consist of Nadi Shodhan, Bhramari pranayama, and Bhastrika pranayama.

If those are finished proper, pranayama need to supply concord to the spirit, thoughts, and frame while being supervised. This makes you spiritually, mentally, and physical robust.

History of Pranayama

This timeline will provide you with a pinnacle degree view of pranayama's history and its practices. Even in spite of the fact that this list isn't meant to be whole or exhaustive, it does consist of a few ket texts that might hobby genuinely all and sundry who wants to apprehend extra about pranayama's information.

"Brihadaranyaka Upanishad – seven hundred BCE"

While the phrase prana end up determined in Chandogya Upanishad as early as 3000 CBE, information regarding a respiration exercising that they name pranayama didn't arise till lots later, somewhere spherical seven-hundred BCE.

The earliest recorded connection with pranayama respiration may be placed within the Brihadaranyaka Upanishad in hymn 1.Five.23. This links respiratory to regulating our life strain.

There aren't each different hints for strolling inside the route of pranayama within the Upanishad. But the concept that respiration can assist a person reach immortality and higher health is repeated continuously in a few unspecified time inside the future of yogic teachings and texts.

"The Bhagavad Gita – 5th Century to second Century BCE."

You can also find pranayama referred to inside the Bhagavad Gita. The textual content in economic wreck four and verse 29 highlights the use of conscious exhaling, inhaling, and breath retention to get into a trancelike country. This textual content furthermore says that working towards pranayama regularly can help a person gain more control over their experience with the useful resource of "curbing the consuming technique."

"The Maitrayaniya Upanishad — Fourth Century BCE"

This might be the critical pranayama textual content because it houses the earliest reference to pranayama as one a part of a larger, multifaceted gadget. It end up probable written loads of years earlier than the Yoga Sutras of Patanjali, which taught about union, reasoning, meditation, recognition, sensory withdrawal, and breath control utilized in yoga.

Pranayama is stated explicitly in chapter six and verse 21. It explains that you can obtain deliverance by using the usage of the usage of super respiratory retentions even as focused on saying "Om" to assist prana circulate the power channels.

"Patanjali's Yoga Sutras – one hundred to 4 hundred CE"

Many pupils will agree that this newsletter is a compilation of texts from all the sooner yogis. By the time Patanjali became a yogi, yoga has tailor-made and grown to severe measures. Where the Maitrayaniya Upanishad has spoken of the six-limbed tool, it have become elevated to an eight-limbed tool, which blanketed niyama, asana, Yama, and pranayama with 4 one-of-a-kind stages of meditative absorption which is probably Samadhi, dhyana, Dharana, and pratyahara.

This text references pranayama in verses 2.29 thru 2.Fifty three in the Sutras. While Patanjali doesn't dive deep into what prana is, it statistics some elements of the breath like retention, exhales, and inhale. It additionally talks about pranayama in verse 2.Fifty one that explains that it is going past all the others.

Plus, it notes numerous advantages of working towards pranayama. Some of those benefits encompass better recognition and higher bodily fitness. Concentration is a deeper state of yoga. Within verse 2.Fifty , it talks about how a pranayama exercising can dissolve or reduce the veil that covers the "internal illumination."

Benefits of Pranayama

The key to having a happy and healthy lifestyles would likely genuinely lie within the manner you breathe. If you could research to take care of your breath, it could deliver you lower back to the existing, make you enjoy calmer, and make you extra privy to yourself.

Pranayama can purify the nadis or psychic channels and allows intellectual and bodily stability. It can purify over seventy ,000 channels inside the frame. It can purify the respiration and blood systems. Deep respiratory can improve the blood with oxygen. Vast portions of oxygen receives to the capillaries, coronary coronary coronary heart, lungs, and thoughts.

Pranayama takes it one step extra than simply being aware about your breath. It makes use of nice strategies and rhythms to provide you numerous benefits in your bodily, emotional, and intellectual states.

- Could slow down the getting old

- Rejuvenates the thoughts and body

- Immune tool booster

- It brings positivity and enthusiasm

- Increases strength

- It receives rid of mind fog

- Improves hobby and reputation

- Reduces tension and concerns

- Calms the thoughts

Pranayama techniques can help cope with a big kind of issues related to pressure like:

- Improving physical health via schooling unique yoga asanas

- It can assist with weight reduction

- Changes the cardiorespiratory gadget and permits decrease blood stress

- It allows get rid of unnecessary mind that can loosen up your overactive mind that help lessen despair and tension

- It lets in relieve bronchial allergies signs

- Improve autonomic features

- Breathing deeply while focusing in your breath may be very rejuvenating and exciting.

- Doing this often can beautify your nation of mind, memory, and interest

Psychology Today described breathing as "an notable possibility to mindfulness you in no way heard of." They additionally stated it "want to assist those those who can't be inactive due to the reality it's miles an energetic meditation."

There were extra than sixty 5 research finished on combining Sudarshan kriya and pranayama breathing. They demonstrated many one in every of a kind health advantages.

Regulates Emotions

Pranayama respiratory can help someone alter their feelings. In a conference held in Germany, the founder of the "Art of Living Foundation," Sri Sri Ravi Shankar, described how emotions and breathing are associated.

- If we recognize our breath's rhythm, we're able to manipulate our thoughts, we ought to manipulate poor emotions along with greed, jealousy, and anger, on the same time as we are smiling from the coronary heart.

- If you determine with a theatre employer, you recognize that after a director asks you to start breathing faster, you may display which you are indignant. If you want to reveal a relaxed and serene mind, you'll be advised to breathe sluggish and gentle.

- The breath has been associated with feelings. There can be a positive rhythm to the breath for each emotion. Even despite the fact that we will't harness the real feeling, you could address them together together with your respiration.

One take a look at executed by means of the use of Phillipot showed that respiration styles that mimic happiness, unhappiness, and anger, can create the identical emotional nation inner us.

This is the principle that pranayama works with. Instead of letting our emotions trade our respiration styles, we should exchange the nation of our emotions by means of the use of being capable of use our breath skillfully. Since it's far difficult to control emotions, if we use pranayama strategies to exchange negative and overpowering feelings, it could grow to be a powerful device to beautify our inner peace and nicely being.

Shallow or Deep Breathing

Take a minute right now and turn out to be aware of your breath. Is it uneven, smooth, shallow, or deep? You can study the proper manner to respire with the aid of manner of manner of searching how new child babies breathe. Have you noticed how their bellies upward push and fall lightly at the same time as they breathe inside and outside?

Most adults breathe from their chest. This form of breathing is shallow, and it sends the mind a sign that we are confused, and something is inaccurate. But if we're capable of discover ways to breathe deeply from our stomach, it may growth breathing, making sure an super supply of oxygen gets to our mind and tells it that the entirety is first-rate.

Take a few other minute and end up aware about your respiration one greater time. Since you have been considering it, has it have been given any smoother or longer?

Difference Between Breathing Exercises and Pranayama

Many people name pranayama respiration physical sports but now not every respiratory exercise can be known as pranayama. Most breathing wearing activities aren't pranayama. Pranayama way "boom of life pressure and its reason is to enhance the body's functionality to preserve and increase prana inside the frame."

If we need to increase our functionality to keep prana, doing pranayama sporting sports can cleanse our nadis or power channels. By often operating closer to pranayama, these channels can turn out to be purer, and our our our bodies can keep more prana, and our minds can meditate and listen higher. Regularly training pranayama can wake up our internal religious stress, deliver pleasure at the same time as enhancing spiritual development.

To boom and hold our lifestyles force, pranayama uses five tools:

- Locks or bandhas

- External retention or bahayia kumbhaka

- Internal retention or antar kumbhaka

- Exhalation rechaka

- Inhalation or poorak

When any workout consists of retentions along side locks, can we have the ability to talk about pranayama? Most of the respiratory sports activities people do are an easy version of pranayama. This may be completed via manner of doing away with the out of doors retention and locks or keeping your breath after exhaling.

Regular Breathing and Pranayama

Everyone knows a manner to respire, even new infant infants. Nowadays, most people need to take a respiratory magnificence to help us cope with our every day lives, anxiety, anxiety, depression, driving, and paintings. Most people understand that deep respiration have to assist overcome life's stresses, so we should understand the technological understanding in the lower back of breathing, pranayama.

Pranayama is an trouble of yoga that teaches us a manner to control and extend our inhaling severa methods. It can train us a manner to alternate the sample, charge, and depth of our respiratory.

Pranayama is being consciously aware of your breath. It is proper rhythmic, deep, and sluggish respiration. It could make more potent the respiration tool. It can soothe the worried machine. It can boom your concentration. Our breath connects our spirit, mind, and body.

Your breathing charge will exchange in step with the conditions round you want. It might probably increase because of a physical or emotional disturbance, but it will sluggish down at the same time as you are non violent and calm. If you get worn-out while mountain climbing some of stairs, you'll get breathless. Try to do this to adjust your respiration so you received't feel as tired. While you're mountain climbing the stairs, hold your shoulders directly. Breathe in deeply for two stairs, and then breathe out for 2 stairs. Continue a rhythm of in and out. By doing this, you may take away extra carbon dioxide even as taking in extra oxygen, and also you obtained't get as tired.

Most of the time, you quality use a fraction of your lung functionality at the same time as you are taking shallow breaths. You aren't growing your ribcage all the manner. Your shoulders are usually hunched, and you've got were given tension for your neck and higher decrease back because we don't have sufficient oxygen in our our bodies, which makes us worn-out and breathless. Try to hold your shoulder blades near collectively with out straining and breathe out slowly and clearly. You want to make certain you push all the air out of your lungs. Pause and then inhale in a mild, slow, deep breath till your lungs are virtually stuffed. Now breathe out via your nostril without transferring your shoulder blades. Continue doing this as frequently as you can. When you do that, your thoughts is getting stimulated and could dispose of any tensions due to the truth you're giving your body a higher oxygen supply.

Kinds of Breathing

Abdominal Breathing: these are deep stomach breathing on the way to deliver sir into the most important and lowest a part of the lungs. Breathing is probably deep and gradual so that your diaphragm receives used properly.

Thoracic Breathing or Chest Breathing: you perform this breathing via contracting and growing simply the chest while you control your stomach. This definitely activates the center a part of the lungs.

Clavicular Breathing or Sectional Breathing: This is a shallow respiration method in which the belly is controlled, and you breathe through forcing air into the higher part of the lungs. Your collar bones and shoulders are raised on the identical time as your stomach is being shriveled even as you inhale.

A whole pranayama breath will integrate all the above, beginning with the stomach and continuously inhaling thru the thoracic and onto the clavicular place. Your stomach wants to enlarge out on the same time as you inhale after which settlement while you exhale. In order to recognize this motion higher, sit down down in a meditative posture; Vajrasana will be high-quality, placed your fingers on your stomach. Breathe out slowly, and then breathe in through your nose. Move your arms a ways from each particular whilst your stomach bulges. Now you may preserve this breath for a 2nd or two. Slowly breathe out, so your belly retracts and brings your palms nearer together. Hold this breath for a second or and repeat this respiration cycle five times. You can use this ratio of inhaling for a preserve in thoughts of 4, preserve for a matter wide variety of , breathe out for a depend of eight, and hold for 2. Your respiration wants to be rhythmic, sluggish, and deep.

The lower additives of your lungs will growth with the airflow. The rhythmic actions of your diaphragm will lightly rub down the belly and could assist your organs function higher.

Pranayama wants to be completed at the same time as sitting in a powerful posture like Ardhpadmasana or Padmasana and desires to be executed with an empty belly and early inside the mornings. Try your first-rate to find an area this is properly ventilated. Your breathing wants to be rhythmic and slow. Your eyes want to be closed so you can control your body and mind. You may be the use of the components of inhalation or poorka, retention or kumbhaka, and exhalation or rechaka.

Kinds of Pranayama:

- Kapalabhati Pranayama: this breathing will exhale air from your lungs a bit forcibly however will help you inhale involuntarily

- Bahya Pranayama: for this breath, you may breathe in forcibly, breathe out, after which preserve your breath

- Shitali Pranayama: that is a cooling breath

- Bhastrika Pranayama: this breath forces the air outside and inside

- Brahamari Pranayama: this is the humming bee breath

- Anulom Vilom: that is an alternate respiratory method

- Ujjayi Pranayama: that is the effective breath

Breath and Mind

The manner you breathe can allow you to recognise about your modern-day u . S . A . Of thoughts. You might be feeling appropriate about yourself, you're considering having cocktails with some friends after art work. You might be feeling pressured because of the fact you are attempting to get the entirety

32

to your "inbox" into your "outbox" earlier than your day ends.

All strain isn't awful, however in case you run on immoderate-octane continuously, you may emerge as a candidate for a big burnout. Short-term stress is probably extremely good because it will can help you gain that last date. If you rely upon quick-term stress every day, you may discover that your body gets worn out. Your immune device receives impacted, and your memory, hobby, and mind might be impaired with the useful resource of extended-term pressure.

This is on the same time as your respiration comes into play. It can restore you. It will permit you to keep electricity for those moments in existence whilst you need your highbrow sources.

Your breath can have an impact in your mind and brain. You can look at hundreds if you could learn how to take a look at your breath and word what is going on. Let's communicate approximately our nose. Why can we have nostrils? All we need is one huge hole. There is a motive why we have nostrils. If you breathe via the left nostril, it'll interact the right facet of the brain. If you breathe via the proper nostril, it'll interact the left element of the thoughts.

Researchers have placed that after we breathe thru the right nose, our body's metabolism engages instances as heaps as compared to respiratory thru the left nose.

You understand that once we had been born, we inhaled deeply and commenced crying. The very last element that we will do in advance than we die is to take one remaining breath out, and then different people will begin crying. When you were born, you cried, however everyone else laughed. When you die, you may take in your remaining breath, and every person else will cry. If that doesn't appear, you haven't lived your notable life.

In our each day lives, we forget about our breath. There are four resources of power:

- Calmness: that is a pleasing or glad country of mind

- Breath: this is the awesome deliver of electricity. Our breathing should help us energize our whole tool. If you're tired, attempt some deep respiratory or alternate the manner you're respiration, you'll in all likelihood truely experience more energetic.

- Sleep: strive now not dozing for absolutely one night time and notice how nicely you revel in the following morning.

- Food: fast for a few days, and you could recognise what I'm speakme approximately. If you eat an excessive amount of or too little, you'll drain your power

Just taking a few minutes and meditating will energize your device. Normally, humans expect that meditation is much like attention, however this isn't proper. Meditation is the complete opposite of concentrating. Concentration is what you get whilst you meditate.

The Science Behind It

If you could observe subjects properly, you could see a rhythm in nature; the seasons are a rhythm in nature. Our our our bodies have a rhythm, too. You may additionally have found which you get hungry at the equal times every day. You get sleepy at the same time; this is referred to as a biorhythm. No you can liberate your smartphone however you.

There is a rhythm for your breathing. It can be distinct all through the morning, midnight, and whilst you encounter severa feelings. If you sense satisfied or fragrance your chosen flower, your respiration might be robust, consistent, and slow, and your exhale will dissolve. If you experience indignant or aggravated, your exhale can be lots more potent.

There is a rhythm in your notion patterns and feelings. Your respiration will alternate with all the numerous emotions. It will be exquisite on the equal time as there may be anger or fear. It all is predicated upon on how pressured you are, and there is probably a rhythm inside the changes interior you.

Your respiration can deliver concord to those rhythms, and then lifestyles becomes track. It will take you three days and three hours to research this. After you've got got observed this, you can best want to exercise this for ten minutes each day. If you are a pupil and function an exam arising, respiration will will let you stay calm and decorate your instinct.

Does strain reduce sturdiness? Stress doesn't reason mortality, but it is able to have an effect on us in diverse techniques. If pressure hormones boom, we are more at risk of ailments and illnesses. You might be dwelling, but you'll be very sick. Relieving your strain goes to keep you wholesome.

How can someone use breathing and meditation to deal with pain or lessen all the horrible impacts of stress? There have been heaps and thousands of human beings who have gotten a deal with on their despair through the usage of breathing techniques. It may be used as an possibility to taking antidepressants.

Has there constantly been a connection among our minds and our breath? This connection is as vintage as the relationship among our breath and our frame. It is going lower again to the start of time.

This connection has been there in each historical lifestyle. If you ever get the hazard to have a look at the Maoris in New Zealand, they'll greet every other thru converting a breath. They will rub each other man or woman's nostril, inhale, and exhale. This is the manner they be a part of and make harmony among people.

Buddha told us truly to study our breath or Anapanasati. This can help you have a look at each sensation and goes beyond to appearance your real nature. Your breath doesn't have a faith or nationality. All of humankind need it.

Breath and Life

Ancient yogis observed that the respiration price did correlate with how prolonged we stay and our fitness. They concept that to live to antique age, a person had to breathe slowly. To display you this idea in extra element, we are going to speak approximately the animal nation. Humans do fall underneath primates which incorporates apes and monkeys within the taxonomic order. We ought to teach ourselves to respire effectively by using way of the usage of jogging closer to pranayama.

Never Pant Like Dogs

Among the vertebrates, the big tortoise might be the oldest dwelling animal. Dogs breathe very rapid and are on the overall opposite facet of the spectrum. They have a concise lifestyles span. Dogs will breathe 20 to 30 times every minute and live among ten and a long term.

The massive tortoise nice breathes 4 times each minute and can stay to be a hundred and fifty years antique. The oldest dwelling tortoise have become idea to be over 250 years vintage. A tortoise named "Jonathan" is at 186 years right now and is the oldest living animal appeared to man. From this factor on, in case you see that you are respiration fast, try to take some slower breaths.

Breathe Consciously, Breathe Slow

We take respiratory as a right because it's miles one of the many stuff that we do mechanically, together with our heart beating or our frame temperature staying the equal. This is all controlled with the aid of our concerned tool, and our breath isn't some aspect that you have to be aware about each minute of each day. Used efficaciously, it may assist alternate your united states of america. Your breath is a tool that works on every your thoughts and frame.

Having a slower respiration fee can virtually have an effect in your mood. It turns off the chemical materials which can be created through responding to strain. It can growth the immune gadget in your frame. Anytime you get pressured, you could commonly have shallow breaths coming out of your chest. This can motive hundreds of harm over the years. If our pressure turns into chronic, we need to take manipulate to preserve away illnesses and ache. If you have got got were given manipulate over your respiratory, you have determined the crucial thing to your highbrow and bodily health.

Even if you are walking out or truely strolling, it is great to preserve your thoughts calm and your tongue in your mouth. Focusing on breathing in thru your nose and out through your mouth is the first-rate manner to address more demanding and longer responsibilities.

If you definitely breathe inner and out via your mouth, it'll faucet into your sympathetic stressful device and cause your flight or fight reaction. This would possibly artwork if you have to run a sprint, and also you want to transport as fast as possible, but mouth respiration can deplete your frame's responses.

Slow Breathing Is Healthy

An common human will breathe among 12 to 18 times every minute. This is what each first useful aid e-book will let you know. Breathing about 12 instances is excellent, however whilst you hit 16, your body is experiencing some strain.

With extra superior yogis and healthful, energetic people, a everyday breath price might be plenty decrease, contributing to an extended life. A decrease breath fee will reduce the coronary coronary heart's pressure and maintain it going for loads, many years. When you upload a few bodily sports whilst respiration, it is able to stretch your frame's ability to address strain. The frame's strain response does have its limits. When it has to stop, there's a point that turns off the hormones that assist you to deal with your strain triggers. Your frame is going to need a while to get higher.

Pranayama Terminology

There are many extraordinary phrases which you have come upon already and will come across all through this e-book. To ensure which you absolutely understand what all of them endorse, we're able to pass over some vital phrases that you need to realise.

Ajapa – Ajapa is a type of meditation technique that places reputation on the natural sound of your breath. This meditation exercise is taken into consideration a shape of yoga. Broken down, the word comes from "a," that means "now not," and "japa," meaning "repeated." That approach the phrase manner "no longer repeated." Within the context of this yoga, japa refers to the effortful repetition of the sound. That way ajapa is the accessible repeated sound, like someone's natural breath. With sufficient practice, manipulate your breath's sound thru this yoga is thought to create feelings of kindness, compassion, and peace.

Anasakti Yoga – Anasakti yoga is a manner of lifestyles and philosophy endorsed with the aid of Mahatma Gandhi. It encourages people no longer to create an attachment to the fabric global. Anasakti yoga teaches you the manner to allow pass of attachments because of someone's movements. It is idea that non-attachment will help free up people from suffering. The practitioner won't be sure with the beneficial resource of attachment to the fabric worldwide, for this reason supporting them discover eternal lifestyles. Those who exercise this form of yoga stays really devoted to and engaged of their art work and movements, but they don't have any attachment to the final results.

Apana – Apana is the second one maximum critical vayus or sorts of prana inside Hatha yoga. Vayu, in Sanskrit, approach "wind" and refers to how prana moves through the frame. Apana vayu regulates your prana's outward waft and is on top of things of the elimination of physical wastes and pollution. This is located within the pelvic ground and spread as heaps as the lower stomach, regulating reproductive talents and digestion.

Arhatic Yoga – Arhatic yoga is a gadget for religious growth created to help human beings evolve their souls quicker to serve humankind and the Earth. This yoga system consists of breathing techniques, meditation, asanas, and spiritual practices which is probably brought together into a unmarried cohesive gadget.

Ashtanga – Ashtanga yoga is a very bodily form of yoga created thru manner of T. Krishnamacharya and Sri K. Pattabhi Jois. It was derived from Hatha yoga. Ashtanga technique "8 limbs" and refers back to the eight-fold course or 8 yoga limbs referred to in the Yoga Sutras. It is a dynamic, flowing style so that you can connect the body and the breath. This method stresses the reality you need to exercise each day.

Bhastrika – Bhastrika is bellows breath and is a form of pranayama. It is considered one of the maximum essential respiration strategies.

It is derived from the Sanskrit word for "bellows" due to how the belly pumps the breath. It calls that allows you to take rapid and powerful inhales and exhales, a good way to make an audible sound. It can assist cleanse the airways and growth the electricity of the mind and body.

Bindi – Bindi is a mark of safety that many Hindus put on in the middle in their brow. It comes from the phrase Bindu, that means dot or component. Bindu refers back to the aspect in which introduction began, and the bindi they put on symbolizes that. Traditionally, the bindi is white, pink, or yellow.

Desa – Desa originates from a Sanskrit phrase that translates to u.S. Of the united states, place, or location. In traditional Indian way of life, desa is the same as the county. It is a geo-cultural unit. Within yoga, desa is the area within the frame, especially in terms of respiratory sports. Desa is also a manner to address imbalances or sicknesses inside the frame indoors Ayurveda.

Egoism – Egoism is a conduct display that is inspired thru a person's self-hobby. It furthermore refers back to the concept that self-interest is the premise of all ethical behavior.

Hasta Vinyasa – Hasta vinyasa is a chain of actions in yoga that includes arm actions. It comes from hasta, meaning "usual with the palms," and vinyasa, which means "coordinated movement."

Hatha Yoga – Hatha Yoga Pradipika turned into written within the fifteenth century with the aid of the usage of Swami Svatmarama. It is the oldest surviving manual of Hatha yoga and is taken into consideration one of the three most vital yoga texts. Hatha yoga is supposed to influence the practitioner thru the eye in their body to the Self's recognition. It is made from asanas, pranayama, mudras, bandhas, and Samadhi.

Kosha – Koshas are taken into consideration the five layers of focus that veil the proper self. To discover every layer enables to bring you in the direction of oneness with the proper self and universe. Kash way "shielding" or "sheath." That's why the koshas are often referred to as the 5 sheaths. Practicing yoga will take a person deeper into the self via the koshas.

Kripalu Yoga – Kripalu Yoga is a modern yoga fashion that have come to be tailor-made from ancient Hatha practices. It is made of sequences of asanas in no effective order and rest and respiratory sports activities. This yoga wants to assist manual your recognition inward to recognition at the flow of prana.

Kundalini – Kundalini approach "coiled one." It refers to a primal pressure that lives "coiled" at the bottom of your spine. Different yoga poses, meditation, and managed breathing can help wake up the kundalini and enlighten your chakras.

Manipura – Manipura is the call for the sun plexus chakra. Mani translates to "gem," at the same time as Pura method "town." That literal interprets the phrase to the "metropolis of jewels." That permits us to consider this chakra as our non-public treasure and center of wellness.

Mudra – Murda is a form of symbolic and sacred gesture that is located in yoga. One of the maximum well-known mudras is used inside the route of meditation and yoga practices to help channel the flow of prana. It interprets to seal, gesture, or mark. Across one of a type traditions and religions, there are spherical four hundred mudras. Each one has a very precise symbolism and is notion to have a particular impact at the mind and body.

Nadi – Nadi interprets to drift, tube, or channel. It is the community of channels through which your strength travels. The kind of nadis that a person has relies upon on the lifestyle, but there appear to be 3 main nadis that flow into within the route of the spinal wire and chakras.

Pavan – Pavana manner air and is one of the five elements of the universe. In the Hindu perception, the ones five factors will dissolve upon lack of existence. The specific factors are Aakash (sky), Agni (fireplace), Jala (water), and bhumi (earth).

Pingala – Pingala is one of the nadis of the astral frame. It is positioned from the right nostril and runs right all the way down to the idea chakra. It runs along the proper element of the spinal twine. It is goal, rational, analytical, and can be competitive.

Prana – Prana is a Sanskrit phrase with several English translations, collectively with vital principle, strength, and lifestyles pressure. It refers to all the manifesting energy inside the universe and is present in living subjects and inanimate devices.

Rasa – Rasa manner fluid, sap, or essence. Spiritually, it refers to the essence of human revel in. It is the emotions that govern our lifestyles. Tantric beliefs have nine primary human emotions. Within yoga, high-quality 3 of the rasas are concept to be essential.

Samadhi – This is the final step alongside the course of yoga. It interprets to liberation, bliss, and enlightenment. In Buddhism and Hinduism, it's far seen due to the fact the top of all highbrow and religious interest.

Shodhana – This Sanskrit word manner purifying or cleansing. It is frequently paired with Nadi. Nadi shodhana is a calming breathing exercising that allows to relieve anxiety, strain, and fatigue.

Sitali – This Sanskrit word translates to soothing or cooling. It is generally used to explain a form of pranayama. With sitali, the tongue can be rolled, and the breath is pulled in thru the tongue as in case you have been breathing through a straw.

Tantra Yoga – Tantra is a sort of yoga that uses unique rituals to discover approximately the universe thru the human microcosm. It seeks to balance out human instincts to reap enlightenment.

Tapasya – Tapasya literal manner "generation of heat and electricity." It includes strength of thoughts, moderation, deep meditation, and efforts to discover Self-recognition. Gurus and priests in Hinduism, Jainism, and Buddhism exercising this to acquire non secular liberation.

Yogini – This refers to a woman yoga draw near. Its male counterpart is yogi. It translates to the enlightened goddess.

Yuj – Yuj way to sign up for. The phrase yoga comes from, that may be a religious, physical, and intellectual exercising that originated in ancient India. Yuj is yoga's root word, it really is that yoga seems to unite the spirit, frame, and mind.

Precautions

There are some precautions that you want to take earlier than you begin going for walks in the course of pranayama:

- You have to in no way exercise pranayama in case your lungs are congested.

- Make certain you do pranayama in a room this is nicely ventilated, or exercise it outside.

- You want to in no way exercising pranayama in a rush.

- If you frequently workout pranayama and asanas, do your asanas in advance than you do pranayama. After you exercising your asanas, lighten up in a Shavasana pose in advance than you do your pranayama. Don't perform a touch thing strenuous after you've got completed your pranayama.

- Never practice pranayama if you revel in tired. Try to relax for 15 mins inside the Shavasana pose earlier than doing all of your pranayama.

- If you are feeling any soreness or tiredness, forestall the pranayama. Lie down within the Shavasana at the same time as respiration typically. Talk to a yoga professional in advance than beginning your pranayama.

- If you're a amateur at pranayama, you shouldn't maintain your breath. Once you have got grow to be comfortable with the pranayama fundamentals, you may discover ways to maintain your breath on the same time as being guided via an expert after learning yoga respiration basics.

- It may additionally need to assist in case you did no longer exercise pranayama right after you have eaten. You will need to attend approximately three hours while you eat. Heavy food are going to take plenty longer to digest. If you do your pranayama for the duration of the night time, consume a healthy snack that may be digested by the point you begin your pranayama.

- Don't make any loud sounds at some stage in your respiration. Make fantastic your breathing remains everyday and rhythmic.

- You need to in no manner stress for the duration of your pranayama practice. Your lungs are very delicate. Make sure your breathing isn't compelled past its limits.

- Always breathe thru your nose till you are recommended not to acquire this.

- Pranayama desires to be practiced after you have got got acquired manage over your frame with the aid of studying all of the asanas. Practicing pranayama will generate power internal your frame, at the equal time as yoga asanas get rid of the blockages that preserve the frame's strength flowing.

- If you have were given were given any continual scientific conditions, ask your yoga instructor and health practitioner in advance than your start pranayama.

- If you have got a hernia, immoderate blood stress, or coronary heart disease, you have to in no manner do bhastrika or Kapal Bhati pranayama. If you are doing kapalabhati and are a beginner, make certain you exhale very gently and in no way use excessive pressure.

- If you have got got low blood pressure, by no means do skitkari pranayama. Never do this pranayama throughout the iciness months.

- Never do suryabhedi at some stage in the summer time months.

- Never do chandrabhedi all through the wintry climate months.

- Those who've a hernia or immoderate blood stress should no longer practice agnisar pranayama. Never do this pranayama after you've got had surgical treatment in your belly.

Chapter 2: The Importance Of Correct Breath

I stated in the appearance that people don't breathe efficaciously. However, except we are physical out of breath, most oldsters don't recollect how we breathe. This is why many of us are respiratory incorrectly and use simplest about a third of our lungs. Studies have determined that this will be the purpose of numerous health issues. When we don't breathe definitely, it leaves us feeling drained, depressed, demanding, compelled and influences our sleep.

In a unmarried day, we breathe approximately 20,000 instances. It lets in the immune, cardiovascular, digestive, muscular, and anxious structures. Around 70% of the pollutants in our frame leave thru our breath. The lungs' primary function is to move the oxygen inside the air we breathe to enter our pink blood cells. The crimson blood cells then deliver the oxygen inside the course of the body. The lungs moreover assist to do away with CO_2 whilst we exhale.

There are numerous respiratory errors that human beings make that constrict lung functionality. These embody:

- Unconsciously preserving the breath

Signs of keeping your breath can be sighing greater than trendy, it really is your body's way of getting greater oxygen, particularly while you are traumatic or strain. You will probable be a chest breath and experience a tightness for your shoulders and neck.

- Breathing through your mouth

Breathing through the mouth in desire to the nose is a very commonplace addiction which could purpose you to revel in tired and offer you with a dry mouth. When you don't breathe properly via your nose, it can modify your blood strain and coronary coronary coronary heart fee. It moreover will increase your pressure response. Nitric oxide is likewise produced within the nose, which, as soon as inhales, considerably improves their capability to take in oxygen. This is extremely vital on the identical time as you are exercising.

To assist you parent out if you are breathing well or not, the following are 4 signs and signs and symptoms of wrong respiratory. After that, you may find out six assessments you could do to peer if you are respiratory improperly.

The first sign of horrible breathing is often yawning. Yawning is commonly prompted even as you're tired, but it is able to additionally be brought on through shortness of breath or shallow breathing. This is in particular real in case you are obese or if you have fitness troubles.

The 2nd sign is that you grind your teeth whilst you are dozing. When you breathe incorrectly, it's miles frequently accompanied via enamel grinding due to the fact every of those are common symptoms of pressure.

The 0.33 sign is which you have a tightness in your shoulders and neck. Around 80% people are top chest breathers. Instead of taking deep breaths, we take shallow breaths, which motives the muscle tissues in the back, shoulders, and neck to overcompensate, and will tighten up to assist the frame breathe deeper simply so the lungs can get extra air.

The fourth signal is that you continually enjoy worn-out. The maximum not unusual side effect of incorrect breathing is that you feel tired due to the truth you could't get right of entry to sufficient of the respiration device.

With that during mind, permit's attempt these exams for fallacious respiration.

1. Upper-Chest Breathing

You will lie to your yet again and location one among your hands on your top chest and the opportunity to your belly for this test. Lie right here for a couple of minutes and have a study how your arms go with the flow. If the hand in your chest moves while you breathe, however the one in your belly doesn't, then you definately are a chest-breather. Anything more than a moderate motion out of your chest shows that you can no longer be breathing efficiently.

2. Shallow Breathing

Again, you could deceive your once more for this check and place your hands spherical your lower ribs, one hand on either side. As you breathe, you need to experience an handy enlargement of the ribs as you take a breath in and a gradual draw back as you launch the breath. If the ribs don't float, then your breath is honestly too shallow, even supposing you may see your stomach shifting.

three. Overbreathing

While you're nevertheless lying down, take a couple of minutes to allow your body to set up a snug breathing charge. Then start to depend the period of your subsequent exhale after which have a look at it to how long the subsequent inhale is. You need your exhale to be a chunk longer. If it isn't, you then definately really are an over breather. For a

2d take a look at, attempt to brief how prolonged your inhale takes. If this causes any type of misery, you're probable an over breather. Since it is easy to control how those tests turn out, you may need to invite any character else to rely range for you at a time on the identical time as you aren't paying attention.

4. Breath Holding

Holding your breath after you are taking an inhale is probably one of the maximum commonplace terrible respiration behavior. To parent out in case you try this, recognition at the transition among inhale and exhale. A breath-holder will normally possibly experience a "lure" and might have a take a look at that they war to begin the exhale. This has a tendency to be greater crucial whilst you exercising. This may be reduced with the useful resource of consciously enjoyable the stomach proper while the inhale ends.

five.   Reverse Breathing

A opposite breath takes vicinity even as the diaphragm receives pulled into the chest whilst you inhale and drops on the same time as you exhale. Lay down and positioned a hand on your belly. Your stomach need to slowly flatten whilst your breath out and rise at the same time as you breathe in. If the possibility takes place, you then definately are a opposite breather. Since this sort of respiration is more likely to take region at the same time as you are exerting yourself, it isn't absolutely dependable.

6. Mouth Breathing

It is pretty easy to tell in case you are a mouth breather. If you aren't sincerely positive, all you need to do is ask a chum or capture yourself whilst you aren't focusing in your breath.

Those sporting activities serve a purpose. You should recognize the way you breathe; that way, you may actively restoration that. This is so important due to the fact respiratory has a bigger impact on our health than we think.

Breathing is so important that humankind lengthy in the past said how treasured it is to survival and the way the frame and mind feature.

As early due to the fact the primary millennium BCE, the religions Tao and Hinduism placed excessive importance on a "important precept" that flows via us, a form of strength, and appeared respiratory as a shape of its manifestation. In Tao, that is known as qi, and the Hindus call it prana, as we've have been given positioned out.

Sometime later, the Greek term pneuma and ruah in Hebrew stated the divine presence and breath. In Latin based languages, spiritus is at the muse of respiration and spirit. Pranayama became the number one shape of breath retention to bring together at the concept spherical controlling the respiratory gadget to assist growth sturdiness.

Johannes Heinrich Schultz, a German psychiatrist, created "autogenic education" inside the Twenties to help people loosen up.

This method emerge as based totally completely actually upon a slow and deep breath and might be one of the West's most well-known respiratory techniques. Several present day types of mindfulness meditation emphasize respiration-based totally totally sports.

Every meditation, relaxation, or calming method is based at the breath, which is probably the bottom not unusual denominator in each approach to calm the mind and body. Research into body shape and the effects of breath-control offers credence to the fee of regulating and tracking our breathing. Even in case you best have a fundamental knowledge of body structure lets in offer an cause of controlled breath induces relaxation. We all apprehend that emotions affect our our our bodies. When we are satisfied, the corners of the mouth will flip up, and the edges of the eyes will crinkle right into a feature expression.

The autonomic hectic device, ANS, connects the mind to the body through a two-manner road. If you're experiencing anxiety or tension approximately things taking region to your life, the mind will set off the sympathetic nervous system thru the nerves of the ANS. This is what is referred to as our combat or flight response. This will purpose your coronary coronary heart to overcome quicker and your breath to increase, amongst particular topics.

Similarly, in case you are stable and calm, at relaxation, or engaged in something you discover excellent, the breath will deepen and sluggish. This is on the same time as you're below the have an effect on of your parasympathetic nervous device, which creates a chilled effect. What is an awful lot tons much less regarded is that the outcomes appear inside the contrary course. The state of the body could have an effect on the emotions. Studies have decided that once your face smiles, the mind will reply in type. This approach you may begin to enjoy more pleasant emotions. Breathing has the identical shape of impact.

The coronary heart and lungs can deliver our brains feedback and inform them that subjects are excellent, regardless of the fact that they aren't. One interesting way this takes location includes the connection our lungs and coronary heart has and their nerves. Every time you breathe in, the coronary coronary heart is advised to triumph over a chunk quicker. When you exhale, the coronary coronary heart slows down a piece. The everyday effect is that there's a slight trade in your coronary heart price every minute.

But in case you take the time to make one part of this cycle longer than the opposite and do this for a few minutes, the gathered effect will both growth or lower your coronary coronary heart price. If the inhales live longer for a couple of minutes, your coronary coronary heart price will boom. This is because it sends a message to the mind that subjects ought to be a bit extra active in the frame and thoughts, stimulating the sympathetic hectic system. The opposite is proper at the same time as you make the exhales longer. The parasympathetic apprehensive device receives delivered on, and the frame tells the thoughts that subjects are proper and sluggish down the frame.

This may be very obtrusive in human beings who have breathing problems. When the ones troubles have a propensity to be acute or sporadic, it may reason a panic assault. If they will be persistent, they frequently spark off a muted anxiety. It is predicted that round 60% of human beings with COPD have depressive troubles or anxiety. These problems in all likelihood stem from worries approximately what the contamination may also additionally come to be doing to them, however in simple terms mechanical factors additionally make contributions to this. The trouble that they revel in regularly consequences in quicker respiratory, which doesn't have with their oxygen supply however will irritate their tension and bodily ache.

Rapid respiration has the electricity to exacerbate and contribute to panic assaults thru the cycle of worry triggering a faster breath, which then will growth fear. Georg Alpers, in 2005, at the facet of the help of his colleagues, found high-quality and unconscious hyperventilation on the same time as a person with a riding phobia headed out at the motorway.

Whether or no longer the tension is attributable to respiratory troubles or exclusive troubles, it may be eased thru a number of respiration strategies derived from Eastern techniques. For example, comply with your breath is a way that turns the attention to the breath and is one of the first additives of mindfulness meditation. When you integrate reassuring thoughts with the breath, you could control your worried device.

Research has located that the vagus nerve and brilliant chemical neurotransmitters are the motives for the outcomes that a trade in respiratory has at the heart fee. Remember that the ANS is simply in search of to keep your historic past systems balanced and strolling efficaciously to the day's ever-changing situations.

Nadi and Svara

Svara is a respiration technique that permits you manage your breath through alternating the breathing cycles via the right and left nostrils. This reason of this is to assist balance the flow of your prana through your strength channels, nadis, so that you can attain spiritual, bodily, and mental health.

Svara is Sanskrit, which means tone or sound. There are fundamental nadis. The ida and Pingala and constitute the airflow thru the right and left nostrils. Yogis have positioned that through this physical connection of ida and Pingala, you could have an impact on the important and intellectual energies in the frame to awaken sushumna. This turn out to be once they came up with the various strategies to balance the svara. There are many techniques to balance the svara, however the primary one is nadi shodhana pranayama, this means that to purify the exceptional electricity network of the nadi in the frame. This is what has end up called trade nostril breathing.

With this pranayam, you set up a respiration sample via the right and left nostrils and consciousness on how the air flows via your nostrils. There are diverse levels of this from clean to trendy, but the essence stays; this respiratory sample stability purifies and tones the energies in the mind and frame. There are also extra specific pranayamas, such as surya bheda, in which the Pingala is stimulated at the same time as you breathe only thru the proper nostril. Chandra bheda while the ida is inspired with the resource of respiratory through the left nostril best.

Diaphragmatic Breathing

Diaphragmatic respiration is a selected breathing exercise that calls as a way to take a deep that clearly engages the diaphragm. The diaphragm is a dome-long-established muscle positioned beneath the lungs and controls your breathing function. When taking a breath in, your diaphragm is pushed downwards. This smooth motion will shape a chain of sports. Next, your lungs will begin to amplify, a tremendous manner to motive horrific stress, drawing air in through your mouth and nose. After you start to release the breath, your diaphragm will push up, in case you want to help to push all the air out of your lungs.

Stress, poor postures, restrictive apparel, and conditions that weaken your respiratory muscle groups can cause a person to grow to be a chest breather. Some research indicates that diaphragmatic respiratory can help those who have COPD. Diaphragmatic respiration manner which you are absolutely engaging your stomach, diaphragm, and belly muscle groups at the same time as you breathe.

Since you're right proper right here, you possibly need to recognize a way to perform diaphragmatic respiratory. This easy method can offer you with a notable basis of what to anticipate inside the pranayama respiratory techniques.

Come into a snug seated feature, or lie down. If you decide to take a seat in a chair, ensure which you have your feet flat on the floor and that your head, shoulders, and neck are snug. You don't want to keep your again stick without delay to the point in that you're uncomfortable, and also you moreover shouldn't be slouching. If you are lying down, place a pillow under the top and knees to be more comfortable. You also can bend your knees if you would love.

Place one in each of your palms to your top chest. When you are breathing and well engaging your diaphragm, this hand want to stay despite the fact that as you are respiration. Place your distinct hand under your ribcage. The epigastric vicinity you sense will assist you experience the diaphragm as you're respiration.

Take a sluggish breath in thru your nostril. You want the air shifting in thru your nostril to make its way down into the lungs in reality so the belly rises. Make fantastic which you don't force or push your ab muscle tissues out. You need the airflow and motion to be easy. This need to simplest use this epigastric place. You shouldn't enjoy as when you have to strain the low-stomach out by way of manner of the use of compacting the muscle groups. You additionally shouldn't experience the hand on your chest circulate that masses.

Release the breath thru your mouth and permit your stomach to lighten up. Your hand in your belly need to fall inward. Don't try to strain your stomach in via clenching or squeezing the ones muscle businesses. Make first-rate you breathe out slowly and via slightly pursed lips. Again, the hand resting on your chest should stay virtually however

If you find out that this feels awkward on the begin, it might be because you are used to respiration on the aspect of your chest. While the frequency in which you do this could range relying for your health, it's far usually achieved 3 times on the start. The majority of humans will select to do it for 5 to ten mins, one to four times each day. If at any point you be aware that you feel dizzy or lightheaded, prevent this respiratory workout and lay down in case you aren't already. This is considered to be a natural way to breathe.

Since diaphragmatic respiration allows you have got interplay the diaphragm, it may offer you with numerous advantages, which includes:

- Promote relaxation

- Reduce oxygen call for

- Lower the blood stress and coronary heart fee

- Improve middle muscle balance

- Strengthen the diaphragm

While diaphragmatic breathing has been known to help human beings with bronchial allergies and COPD, it need to no longer be used as a standalone treatment. It can also assist with tension, but if executed incorrectly, it is able to get worse the signs and signs and symptoms and signs. People with breathing conditions want to be cautious after they first start training this form of breathing. It can start off inflicting extended fatigue and worked respiration. It ought to assist in case you constructed up this practice often to see the blessings.

Breathing Postures

When you exercise the following financial ruin's pranayama strategies, you may need to understand what posture you can use. There are severa specific yoga poses you could pick out from. We'll skip over a number of the maximum common poses that you may use on the same time as training pranayama.

Easy pose (sukhasana)

Easy pose is the terrific pose for the newbie or everyone who hasn't practice yoga. It's referred to as smooth pose for a cause. Easy pose is a easy circulate-legged seated function—it what most grade-university children sit in at some stage in circle time.

Sit on the ground or your mat in conjunction with your legs out within the front of you and your again straight away to get into this characteristic. Slowly fold the right foot under your left thigh after which the left foot beneath your right thigh. Your legs should bypass at mid-shins and no longer on the ankles. Shift your buttocks so that you are for your take a seat down-bones and make sure that your spine is in alignment. You can also location a pillow or bolster below your buttocks to enhance your hips if you are experiencing any discomfort.

This has a tendency to be an incredible pose for every body, however when you have knee problems, which includes arthritis or knee surgery, this role may not be the first rate. Also, when you have a backache, you can not be able to stay on this function for longer than 5 mins.

Hero Pose (virasana)

This is a touch more develop than an smooth pose, and it in all likelihood no longer the high-quality choice for novices.

To get into this pose, begin thru kneeling on the floor. You can vicinity a bolster or folded blanket amongst your thighs and calves if you need to. Make effective your thighs are perpendicular to the floor and convey your inner knees together. Slide your toes out in order that they are barely wider than your hips. The tops of your ft need to be in competition to the ground.

Exhale after which waft once more midway. Your torso want to be leaned slightly forward. Place your thumbs into the bend of your knees, and pull the pores and pores and skin of your calf muscle businesses inside the direction of the heels. Then you must sit down down down the numerous vicinity among your toes.

If you discover that your buttocks don't rest certainly at the ground, increase them on a thick e-book or block placed among your toes. Your sitting bones want to be flippantly supported. You want to have thumb's-width region among your heels and outer hips. Turn the thighs in and push the pinnacle of the thigh bones into the ground. Place your arms to your lap.

Lift your sternum and roll your shoulders up and down the decrease once more. Lengthen your tailbone into the ground so you are anchored into the torso.

This pose should be used with caution via the usage of manner of these who've coronary coronary heart troubles or complications additionally when you have ankle or knee injuries. If you do, you need to avoid this pose besides you have got a few assist from an trainer.

Thunderbolt Pose (Vajrayana)

This is an historical and conventional seated pose and is much like the hero pose that we definitely did. You can flow into this pose much like the hero pose, but the simplest problem which you won't do is separate your feet. Your heels want to stay touching, and your buttocks will rest on pinnacle of them.

Start through kneeling collectively together with your buttocks and hips lifted off of your legs. If you need some more padding, location a blanket below your feet, shins, and knees. Your thighs want to be perpendicular to the floor, and your internal knees should be collectively.

Un-tuck the feet and keep your feet firmly pressed into the ground. With an exhale, come to rest in your heels. Your feet and shins want to be in line, and your ft should now not splay open or turn in.

Keep your lower back right away and produce your shoulders up and backtrack your lower back to loosen up. Keep your collarbones wide and extend your tailbone toward the ground.

Like the hero pose, this want to be averted if you have a cutting-edge or contemporary ankle or knee harm.

Half Lotus Pose (Ardha padmasana)

Everybody thinks approximately the lotus pose with regards to seated yoga poses, however it is extra give a boost to and a pose that some human beings can't do. A actual opportunity is to do the half of lotus pose. While it is a lot much less difficult than the lotus pose, it may no matter the reality that be too tough for absolute novices.

To get into this position, begin through sitting on the ground along aspect your legs immediately out in front of you and your spine immediately.

Bend your proper knee and hug it for your chest. Then take your right ankle over to the crease of your left hip just so the bottom of your foot is pointed inside the route of the sky. The pinnacle of the foot ought to be in competition to the hip crease.

Bend the left knee after which bring the left ankle under the right knee.

Make wonderful that your backbone remains right away, and your shoulders are snug.

This pose have to be prevented if you have any modern hip, ankle, or knee injuries. If your ankles, knees, or hips are tight, you can find it tough to go your legs. Don't pressure yourself into this pose.

Lotus Pose (padmasana)

To get into this pose, begin seated on the floor together in conjunction with your legs extended in the front of you and your again right away.

Bend your proper knee and externally rotate your hip in order that your knee falls to the right. Bring your right ankle into your left hand and the knee for your right hand. Bring your foot to relaxation at the crease of your left leg, pressing the pinnacle of your foot into the hip crease. Bring the proper knee to rest on the ground.

Lean again and then begin to bend your left knee, and draw the left foot towards your proper knee. Hold the left ankle for your right hand and punctiliously carry your left heel into your proper hip crease.

Keep your again immediately, and your shoulders snug.

This pose have to not be utilized by novices or a few issue with ankle, knee, or hip issues.

Don't strain your legs into this characteristic. It is great to transport slowly and mindfully and stop in case you revel in any shape of ache.

Auspicious Pose (swastikasana)

This is a particularly smooth positioned as much as get into and may be held for extended intervals. Some human beings discover this less tough to do than easy pose.

To get into this position, start through sitting at the floor with your legs out in the front of you. Start through folding your left leg in and area the left leg's sole in opposition on your inner thigh of the opportunity leg.

Bend your proper leg and region your right foot in the vicinity some of the calf and left thigh muscle agencies. Hold your left foot through the toes, cautiously pull it up, and positioned it some of the proper thigh and calf.

Make certain that your knees are touching the ground.

This pose want to be avoided with the useful resource of using people who've sacral infections or problems with sciatica to pinch the nerve.

Accomplished Pose (siddhasana)

This is each distinctive smooth novice pose. To get into the pose, start via sitting at the ground and bypass your legs. Place one foot close to the internal thigh and then convey the alternative foot near into the ankle simply so each of the heels are nearly on the midline.

Make superb that your once more is directly and your shoulders are snug. If you want to, you may area a blanket under your hip bones or knees.

Like with easy pose and auspicious pose, be cautious when you have sciatica, knee, or hip issues.

Picking Your Best Pose

You have to pick out out out the notable pose for you and what your frame can do. Never force yourself right into a pose, as this is best going to reason more problems. If the poses we've got got lengthy past over does now not be just right for you, you could generally sit down in a chair, making sure your decrease back does now not relaxation towards the all over again of the chair.

If you do have wholesome hips and ankles, then you could attempt any of the above poses. The most normally used pose is probably smooth pose. The maximum important problem is which you preserve in thoughts that to have a sustainable, wholesome, and energizing enjoy, you select a function to be able to will will let you be cushty.

Chapter 3: Pranayama Breath

Before you start your exercise of pranayama respiration, you need to understand the smooth recommendations of this exercise. Let's going over some of the ones recommendations so that you are organized.

1. It doesn't damage to do some stretches to heat up the frame and get the breath flowing.

2. Always breathe via the nostril besides knowledgeable to do otherwise or if you have a respiratory obstruction. When you breathe, your stomach want to expand at the inhale. The chest need to first-rate flow into barely collectively together together with your breath.

3. Make notable that your face, nostril, and mouth are snug.

4. Don't stress your breath or retentions to very last longer than what's comfortable. If you try to strain it, then it'll first-class agitate your thoughts.

5.   It works higher if each of your nostrils are in addition open. If one side seems to be closed, strive lying on the other aspect of your body for 30 to 60 seconds.

6.   Make wonderful you take note of your limits. You can overdo easy pranayama. It can be that it's now not the right technique for you. If you begin feeling off-middle, spacey, irritable, agitated, or traumatic, forestall, and pass returned for your everyday breath.

With that during mind, what constitutes a entire yogic breath cycle? Let's find out. A full yogic breath will begin with deep and fluid inhalations so that it will fill 3 areas of your torso independently. First, you fill the decrease belly. Then, the mid-phase of the torso can be filled with breath, expanding the ribs and diaphragm. Lastly, the breath will fill the better chest and shoulders definitely because the inhale comes to an give up. This useful and gradual inhale is probably determined through an extended, gradual exhale, freeing the breath from those three sections in reverse order. The entire spherical of yogic breath will encompass one complete inhale, and one entire exhale.

You need to make certain that each the inhale and exhale are fluid and non-prevent. At no element need to you ever sense any shape of strain. Remember that it can take some time to growth a comfortable dating with pranayama, particularly if you have in no manner completed it earlier than. This is why pranayama is considered a exercise. What is extra important is which you set the goal to boom your ability for breathing deliberately, fluidly, and with out battle or anxiety.

To practice complete yogic breath, do the following:

1.   Pick a snug seated function. Ensure that your pelvic bones are rooted into the ground underneath you and that your backbone is at once. You can also lie down if you choose.

2.   Close your eyes and take a moment to settle in. Close your mouth, and breath via

the nostrils. Let the mind quiet and attention on the natural waft of breath. Live inside the gift.

3.   Once prepared, inhale slowly and with cause. Draw the breath deep inside the low belly, starting on the pelvic ground, and slowly permit the breath fill up to the navel after which out and away from the spine. Focus, first, on filling the lower stomach.

4.   As you fill this region with the breath, permit it extend in every course as it movements up towards the navel.

five.   Once this area is crammed, hold breathing in to fill the mid-torso. Continue drawing the breath up, from the navel to the ribs, and permit the breath lightly growth the diaphragm, ribs, and mid-all over again.

6.   Once you have got stuffed the mid-torso with the breath, complete your inhale thru drawing the breath into the top chest, filling the sternum and coronary coronary coronary heart, and then the shoulders and the bottom

of the neck. Feel your collarbones increase a bit.

7.   Allow the herbal pause that may arise at the top of your breath to show up. The surrender to the prolonged, sluggish exhale. Release the breath from the upper chest, all the way down to the mid-torso, and emptying the lower belly. Feel the stomach contract and entice.

8.   Your exhale may be observed through a herbal pause. Let this occur in advance than starting the following spherical.

Practice this for severa rounds, upwards of 15 mins, after which permit your breath to go lower returned to normal earlier than starting your eyes.

Preparing

Before you start any pranayama workout, you have to get your self prepared. The first trouble you need to have a look at is the time of day you must exercising. Typically, pranayama is practiced early in the morning.

This is the time of day even as the frame is rested, and the mind is calm. However, to rouse earlier than you could require you to go to bed in advance. You furthermore must put off distractions like television and unique era to sell rest. Don't worry, despite the fact that; if mornings are proper for you, cooling practices like ujjayi, Nadi shodhana, and dirgha may be performed earlier than you go to mattress.

Consistency is a top notch deal more crucial than the duration. Ensure which you choose out the most practical time as a way to exercising. Even if you may most effective exercising for ten to 15 minutes, as long as you could do it every day, that's all that topics. It is superb if you do your pranayama on the same every day. Doing it concurrently and within the same place will help domesticate the issue to preserve doing it.

Speaking of region, you have to exercising pranayama in a properly-ventilated room. Try to keep away from education underneath a fan or close to an air conditioner, as this may be distracting and might provide you with a sit back. You have to try to preserve this location uncluttered. Make this location sacred to your, smooth, and constant. If you can, you may exercise outside if the weather lets in, and you don't be afflicted through allergies that would impede your workout.

Next, make certain that you haven't eaten something for 3 to 4 hours in advance than your workout. This is why operating closer to first factor within the morning is terrific. It is tough to carry out breathing strategies when you have a complete stomach. The food you consume, how a good buy you ate, and the manner past due you ate the night time before goes to effect your pranayama the subsequent morning.

Then, you need to make certain you take away all distractions. You have to show off your telephones, don't clearly transfer them to vibrate, and located them away. You additionally want to reveal off and located away laptop structures and pills to get interrupted. If you have got buddies or pals the drop-in or regularly call, tell them of what you're doing now not to break you.

If you're menstruating, practices like nadi shodhana, dirgha, and ujjayi can assist alleviate cramps and special signs and symptoms and symptoms and signs and symptoms at the equal time as lessening fatigue. If you are pregnant, communicate together in conjunction with your doctor and reflect onconsideration on becoming a member of a prenatal yoga magnificence.

Right earlier than your exercising, you could perform a nasal wash. A neti pot might be the nice way to do that.

It's very clean no longer to be ordinary along aspect your workout. These hints can help you realize how you may get started out and what want to reason you to stop practising. Please use the records that will help you make certain you're prepared to help keep away from possible pitfalls in advance than they upward thrust up.

Purifying of Nadis

Within the body, seventy ,000 nadis skip prana to various areas of the frame. However, impurities can motive some of the nadis to prevent going for walks. First, you need to spark off the Nadi, and then you can purify them to preserve prana effectively all over again.

Pingala and Ida nadis can be activated through voluntary respiration techniques, like pranayama. When you purposefully breathe inside and outside with excellent the proper nose, it's going to set off the Pingala Nadi. When you breathe inside and out with high-quality the left nostril, it turns on the Ida nadi.

To awaken Sushmna, you need to find out equilibrium with the ones nadis. Once you achieve a stability among those nadis, it could help facilitate a Kundalini awakening. If you don't acquire a balance, Sushumna will remain closed, and Kundalini will remain dormant. Pingala and Ida's equilibrium is viable great after small nadis, called Nadikas, related to those two essential nadis get purified somehow.

Chapter 4: Preparing For Pranayama

Before we start our breathing wearing occasions, there are some topics which you need to prepare for in advance. You need to make sure that you are inside the proper region, and utilising the right time, to make certain that your regular isn't interrupted, and which you get the most advantage from its exercise. You moreover need to make sure which you are bodily prepped with the proper food regimen and sufficient rest so you can be in the fine situation to interact in a pranayama ordinary. Here in this economic catastrophe we are able to make certain which you look at the splendid way to prepare and optimize yourself on your pranayama respiratory sports.

Creating the Ideal Atmosphere for Pranayama

The Yogi's of old have spoken at super duration close to an appropriate surroundings in which pranayama must be practiced. Some of the hints that the ones historical Indians crafted are in big element beside the point to us in recent times, but one of a kind pieces of advice though keep authentic. Take this piece of historical know-how as an instance, the Yogi's generally informed followers of pranayama, that they need to exercise their respiratory physical sports, "in a province with a robust authorities, ruled by using manner of using a kind, religiously minded ruler, solid government, dominated through way of a kind, religiously minded ruler and inhabited via religious masses."

For maximum in North America and Europe, such instructions are happily with out because of this, but inside the historical global wherein many regions have been trouble to invasion, ruthless dictatorships, and usually chaotic governments, such topics needed to be sorted out! Another piece of advice given approximately proper surroundings is in a good deal the equal vein, putting ahead, that there must be, "no fear of invasion and no disturbance from beasts, thieves, terrible characters, bugs, epidemics, and herbal calamities like draught or floods."

This is over again, a no brainer for optimum oldsters, and is largely setting forward, "Only do Pranayama in places where you acquired't get killed!" If you're making plans on meditating in a back alley of the Bronx in New York, at 3 in the morning, its in all likelihood now not an exquisite concept. I think we are able to all apprehend that. But except primary precautions for bodily protection while wearing out Pranayama, what are we able to do? Number one, discover a pretty place. That manner simply quiet, no TV, no radio, no conversations within the background.

You want to be in an surroundings wherein you can often focus for your respiratory and no longer on specific sounds reverberating spherical you. If your private living environment isn't capable of generate this kind of serenity, quiet corners of nature parks are a brilliant place to exercise, and so are private rooms in public libraries. But anywhere you can pass, really make sure that it's miles the right surroundings for pranayama.

Having Correct Posture and Seating

Next to developing the proper surroundings, the maximum essential aspect for any given respiration workout is to have the right posture and seating at the equal time as you perform it. You have to make certain that the mind, further to the joints, and muscle corporations of the frame are comfortable. If it allows you may need to interact in a few brief stretching in advance than you start. Make nice you sit up, together with your weight calmly balanced on your spine so you can also additionally have the staying energy to see your pranayama session via to the give up.

Your body wants to be regular for prolonged meditative states, and pranayama isn't any outstanding. If you're able, and it acquired't gift any undue scientific issues for you—you may furthermore need to maintain in mind skipping breakfast as well. A entire stomach has a bent to break with the desired posture for pranayama. It is due to this that it is often advised to do pranayama early in the day in advance than eating. Our lung capacity is likewise impacted by means of an entire belly, in preference to an empty one, so absolutely maintain all of those concerns in thoughts earlier than you purchased all of the way down to do your respiratory sporting sports.

Develop a Regular Pranayama Routine

We all have workout routines. Even if it's honestly waking up inside the morning, growing a pot of coffee, and going into the bathe, all of us have set behavior and physical games that interact in in some unspecified time in the future of our life. One of the most essential topics that you can do on your education for pranayama is to truly prep in your private regular routine in your breathing bodily video games as properly. Because the truth is, the blessings of pranayama will in no manner be truely decided out if you handiest do it on uncommon sports.

You need to have regular times in which you may complete your sporting activities. This manner placing apart a selected time every every day, or at the least a few times every week, in which you could engage inside the identical repetitive exercises with out interruption and without hassle. Some clearly enjoy the truth that they are able to have specific instances wherein to focus on this hassle of their life. It allows them to interrupt out for an hour an afternoon on the same time as not having to feel accountable. And if absolutely everyone asks any questions, actually say— "Hey! Give me a ruin dad and mom! It's definitely part of my regular pranayama routine!"

Chapter 5: Practicing Abdominal And Diaphragm Breathing

Whether you simply workout the precepts of pranayama or not, it can't be harassed sufficient without a doubt how vital belly breathing certainly is. The higher we breathe out of our stomach the better that we are able to usually experience. In pranayama, the breath that we breathe into ourselves is known as "Shwas", and the breath that we breath out is known as "Prashwas".

Using Pranayama Crocodile Breath

I recognize that a number of you'll be thinking which you have some thing similar to crocodile breath when you awaken inside the morning however that isn't always what we're speaking approximately right here! When we discuss with pranayama crocodile breath, we are simply regarding a completely precise position that you may region upon the muscle organizations of your diaphragm in order that your respiration can be higher facilitated. In order to vicinity your self into this option you want to place flat to your stomach along side your fingers folded at approximately forty five ranges' immoderate, over each shoulder. It won't be the most comfortable role in the beginning, however your body will quick acclimate to the ideal stressors that this presents.

Once you are in this feature you could feel your body's breath shifting all of sudden thru your diaphragm and your belly. This respiratory workout will paintings to alleviate stomach tension that you could revel in as you drift in some unspecified time in the future of the day. Those that be afflicted via persistent anxiety normally have quite a bit of strain in their belly once they breathe. Colloquially this is called "butterfly's in the belly". So, in case you too can also want to use a remedy from the ones pesky butterfly's you need to supply pranayama crocodile breath a attempt! It will release the tension and set those butterfly's loose!

Attaining the Relaxation Pose

The relaxation pose, or as it's far historically known in pranayama circles, "shavasana", is used to popularity on belly respiration and especially the stomach because it rises and falls at some stage in comfortable and normal breaths. For this exercising, you can lay down, flat for your again, with your head slightly extended through a pillow. Now begin to interest intensely for your breathing, making yourself broadly identified and enjoy every single movement as your lungs fill with air.

Let your rib cage end up free and bendy, even as the muscle groups of your body emerge as nonetheless and without all motion. After you have got carried out this for some time, try raising your fingers over your head as you breathe, serving as an extension of your growing belly as they rise and fall. Do this several times earlier than putting your palms backpedal for your trouble. Now take a second to maintain respiratory with out this more stimulation and display and pay attention to the adjustments on your respiration. You will at once observe a sense of splendid rest.

Upright Abdominal Breathing

Just by means of using sitting up in a chair you may enjoy a great alternate on your normal respiratory ability. From this alteration in characteristic by myself you'll be aware that your respiration does now not revel in find it irresistible does even as you are fame, or mendacity in bed. This a easy indication of your diaphragm and stomach at work, the usage of muscle tissues to help alter breathing in a massive form of bodily poses. You can further decorate some of these strategies with ordinary respiratory bodily activities. To engage in upright abdominal respiratory, placed each hand into onto your thighs as you are sitting upright in a chair.

Now near your eyes and pay specifically interest to your belly and diaphragm as you breathe inside and outside. As you sit down down upright permit your lower again muscle mass tighten barely to hold your posture with minimum effort. You will rapid be conscious your respiration increasing out on each facet of your lungs. You may also see that your belly is increasing with each and each breath. Proceed with this workout for severa more cross arounds, cautiously monitoring the sensations as you enjoy them. You ought to rapid revel in stronger extra not unusual breaths that seem like coming out of your top belly. As you consider your breathing permit your mind to loosen up.

Udara Svasana

Udara Svasana is a traditional respiration technique a good way to permit the enlargement of the abdomen. In this exercise, lay down flat for your again, stretched out on the ground. Next, vicinity your end your stomach button. Now inhale as deep as you in all likelihood can, allowing your belly to seriously make bigger from the air. As you try this, pay especial interest for your stomach button. Watch because it lifts and recedes just like the tides of the sea, and you could quick see tidal waves of rest and relaxation flowing through you. All of the techniques provided on this economic disaster are appreciably beneficial for redirecting respiratory inside the belly and diaphragm. Use them as loads as they may be desired.

Chapter 6: Pranayama Breathing

Pranayama respiration is a surely particular manner to enhance bodily and intellectual stability of the frame. There are numerous strategies that can be explored to help facilitate snug respiratory, however there are only such an entire lot of pages on this e-book! Having that said, we are going to attention on the most critical! Here in this economic damage you could discover the super of the superb, strive all of them!

Bhastrika Pranayama

Also referred to as "bellows breath", "Bhastrika Pranayama" is a shape of respiratory exercising used to help growth your "prana" or as yoga professionals ought to have it—your life strain. Such things aren't to be taken gently. Without tremendous sufficient prana we become gradual, gradual, tried, and depressed. Sometimes we simply want to recharge our prana batteries by using the usage of enhancing our breathing. This exercise will permit you to do without a doubt that. Start off with the resource of manner of placing your self in a sitting posture on a difficult-backed chair.

Raise your self up as excessive as you could at the same time as retaining right, proper away posture within the seat. Now breathe in as deeply as viable, letting your stomach completely extend as you acquire this. After doing this some times, exhale with sudden pressure from your nostrils, in advance than inhaling simply as forcefully. Repeat this numerous times. This will allow you to focus your respiratory sincerely via your diaphragm, permitting you to supply surprising surges of oxygen for your bloodstream, thereby supplying you with a unexpected burst of strength.

I understand that each one this talk of "prana" and "lifestyles pressure" may also furthermore sound like a collection of mystical mumbo at the begin look. But as you could see proper proper here, if we surely trade the terminology, masses of what is practiced in sporting events like this are very lots based totally completely in very actual, physiological science. This is exactly why— regardless of what your private notion machine is probably—the ones yogic practices have some very actual blessings for anyone, if we just provide them a attempt for ourselves.

Kapalbhati Pranayama

This yogic technique of respiration will offer a right away feel of calm and clarity to the thoughts. But rather than prolonged breaths out of the belly, this approach employs a series of targeted, short and effective exhalations, observed via a chain of gentler inhalations. This technique is supposed to smooth out the lungs, and there can be quite a chunk of proof that this method virtually does help to clear out debris from mucous membranes in the breathing device.

This method of respiration is mainly beneficial in case you are tormented by allergies or bloodless and flu symptoms. This exercise has been stated to bring about a "herbal glow" in its members, for this reason the cause within the lower back of the yogic name for it, "skull shining breath". The fine way to rent this exercising is to sit up, together with your hands outstretched toward the ceiling, as you breathe in fast breaths, observed via increasingly more slight, whole inhalations.

Bahya Pranayama

Also referred to as "out of doors respiration" this method of pranayama, focusses on maintaining our respiration outdoor of the frame. How do you do that you might ask? Well—for starters ensure that you feel your diaphragm because it rises and falls, and your stomach as it expands interior and out. Keep a close to recognition on all of those elements of your breathing at some degree within the entire experience. Now exhale with top notch strain, the use of your stomach and diaphragm to squeeze as masses air as possible outdoor of your lungs.

Next, touch your chin to your chest, and try and suck your stomach in as hundreds as you may (if you have ever been fats and attempted to be skinny, you'll in all likelihood recognize a way to try this!) until your stomach is perfectly retracted into your frame. This exercising will leave you with a hollow vicinity right under your ribcage, leaving your belly muscle tissue firmly pressed in opposition to your decrease back! Maintain this characteristic so long as you may. Finally, bring your chin up and start to slowly inhale, letting your lungs completely fill with air. Do this as normally as essential.

Bramari Pranayama

Bramari Pranayama is also every so often called "bee breath" and as you are approximately to look—for proper reason. This form of workout utilizes the vocal cords to create a noisy intonation for the motive of calm. The historical yogic masters likened it to the bumbling of a bee. This respiration workout presents outstanding consolation to any agitation or stress that you will be feeling. Try to sit down as near as you can to a wall or corner, if you need to assist facilitate focus, and sit up in both a chair or right down at the ground.

Now location each certainly one of your index arms into your ear canals, and press down on the cartilage that is living among your ear and cheek. Inhale, and exhale; as you breathe out press down on this cartilage shape collectively with your palms. Do this at the same time as humming as loud as you could, sounding like some issue corresponding to a bee. Repeat this complete technique severa instances till you enjoy better. On the ground this may look like a simply atypical workout, however it genuinely does art work! The handiest problem is, at the same time as you are sitting at your cubicle within the center of the day, keeping your ears and buzzing like a bumble bee, your coworkers certainly can also expect you have misplaced your mind!

I can bear in mind a time I changed into inside the parking zone of a assignment I labored and feature grow to be faced with this form of eventuality. I have become delayed on a undertaking and beneath extreme duress and notion a bit pranayama choose-me-up might assist. As I seemed out on the empty lot I idea I modified into by myself. I didn't see everybody strolling spherical or of their motors, so I figured I had the all clean to do my problem. Well—the whole lot become great, until a protection protect tapped on my window and requested, "Daughter simply what do you located you are—a bumble bee?"

Needless to mention, Mr. Security didn't pretty have the staying power for pranayama! But although, if you can manage it, with out distraction or disruption, this one respiration exercise can do wonders to clean out strain! The moves worried in Bramari Pranayama serve to clean out frazzled nerves and produce lower back readability and reputation, you really ought to supply this one a attempt!

Purna Svasana Pranayama

In order to engage in this breathing exercising seat your self in a cushty feature, it doesn't' take into account in which, it may be on the floor or on the couch. Now raise every cease your head and relaxation your arms on the returned of each shoulder, with each elbow bended towards your head. This feature will assist to make bigger and stretch out your chest muscle corporations to their most quantity. Interestingly sufficient, those which is probably not unusual sufferers of allergic reactions have determined this problem of the workout by myself rather beneficial an amazing manner to assist free them from their frequently-constricted bronchial tubes.

As an bronchial bronchial asthma victim, I can in my opinion vouch for this one myself. I often awaken not able to breathe, feeling like my lungs, or bronchial passages are last up on me. Any allergies patient is privy to genuinely how distressing this feel is. With your bronchial tubes internal your lungs very last up into slim little straws, irrespective of how loads you war to respire and get the air into your lungs, it stays stopped up in the all over again of your throat. Well there may be honestly appropriate facts—due to the fact this workout will assist to open the ones gateways of air simply so oxygen can better are to be had inside and out of the body.

Cleansing Pranayama

For this workout you will need to sit down inner the stylish "lotus" function collectively together along with your legs crossed and your back really at once. Now take your thumb and use it to close your right nostril, together at the side of your nose closed in this way, breathe in through your open left nostril. After you've got were given completed this, open your right nostril and near your left nostril. Now breathe out of your proper nose. Repeat this exercise severa instances earlier than remaining each nostrils and maintaining your breath for about 30 seconds or so.

As you still workout this ordinary try and growth that 30 2d window of shielding your breath for longer and longer periods of time. You can start off your first consultation with just 30 seconds, but then tomorrow, attempt forty five seconds, and the day after that a whole minute. It is of course now not advocated to maintain your broth hundreds longer than a minute. We are in search of to reset and recalibrate the overall universal performance of our lungs despite the whole lot—not seeking to bypass out! At any rate, if performed efficiently, this exercise will serve to help cleanse and calm your body's regulatory structures. It serves to decorate the characteristic of the nasal cavities with regards to the respiration device.

Chapter 7: Tapping Into The Head And Spine Circuits

In Pranayama, the top and spinal circuits consult with the centers of respiratory that live in the head, neck, and spinal column. These circuits ought to be utilized every single day with a view to higher facilitate right pranayama respiration techniques. Here are a number of a number of the maximum critical circuits to utilize.

Spinal Breathing

Sit in a snug feature with every eye closed. Also maintain your mouth near as you inhale deeply despite the fact that your nostrils. Make certain that inhalation starts offevolved offevolved via your abdomen and then proceeds to top off your diaphragm, after which up your spine, for the duration of your collar bones and to your head. This shape of spinal respiration lets in the air to travel right now up your spinal circuit. This will decorate your common respiratory abilities especially. Be exceptional to make spinal breathing part of your pranayama regular as brief as possible.

Lion's Breath

In this breathing exercising you could channel the ferocity of the lion if you want to open up your respiration canal! Sit at the aspect of your legs crossed at the ground and stretch out your fingers along with your arms upraised. Now take a look at once in advance collectively along with your eyes open massive, permit your jaw slowly drop after which set free a lion's roar! Obviously, this method calls for a bit of privacy and can't be achieved in which you'll create a disturbance to others. But at the same time as you may discover a pinnacle region to do it, lion's breath can genuinely serve as a primary consolation to your breathing system. After doing this exercise a few times you could word that your throat is clearer, your eyes are greater targeted, and your massive lung ability has stepped forward. All from a chunk lion's breath!

Dog Breathing

It may also sound a touch bit humorous, however panting like a canine ought to have a few excellent blessings! Tapping into this head circuit will allow you to entice your breath and increase your electricity. And its definitely as smooth because it sounds, if you have a pleasing and private region to exercise, open your mouth, barely distend your tongue and forcefully pant as you breathe within the air. In may not be the maximum attractive difficulty to do, however if you do it for extended sufficient you can see some right now effects!

Applying Chin Lock

For those now not exposed to pranayama, they'll very well be questioning what a "chin lock" can be. In pranayama there are various strategies that we're capable of take advantage of specific head and backbone "circuits" or regions help facilitate our managed respiratory. And this form of strategies to take advantage is to lease some component referred to as "chin lock". Using a chin lock includes placing the frame in a nation of relaxation, and after respiration deep and preserving our breath, bending our head down in order that our chin is firmly pressed, or "locked" into our chest.

After you've got got accomplished this, now straighten out your palms proper inside the the front of you, press your knees collectively, and lock your feature in place. Keep your breath held in, and hold this pose for as long as you in all likelihood are able to accomplish that, in a pretty snug way. Once you have got held the position so long as you're able, you can then loosen up every shoulder, drop your fingers, and raise your head out of the chin lock. Now permit your self to exhale, breathing out sluggish and consistent.

Rest for a 2d and repeat. Harnessing this circuit will will assist you to charge the neural pathways of your head and neck, pumping more blood to the vicinity. It moreover lets in to stimulate your thyroid glands, permitting them to higher do their hobby of regulating the temper and balance of your intellectual state. This technique has additionally been proven to assist lower blood pressure for people who are struggling with higher from high blood stress. Over all, training the chin lock will honestly be assistance to you, if you are stopping in competition to pressure.

Rooting Yourself in Place

123

It is known as both "rooting your self in area" or clearly the "root lock". This meditative pose is completed with the knees accomplishing the ground, and the backbone rigidly locked upright, and in vicinity. Meanwhile the complete frame is to start a way of muscle relaxation with the fingers outstretched in advance than you. It is handiest then that the practice of pranayama can genuinely begin. No depend what form of respiration approach you may be the use of, typically ensure which you are firmly rooted in area earlier than you start—it's far handiest then that the practice of pranayama can really be completed efficaciously.

Chapter 8: The History And Science Of Pranayama

Pranayama is a science within the larger science of Yoga. Although Yoga and pranayama have existed for thousands of years, their existence in the Western consciousness is a few hundred years old, at best.

Additionally, Yoga and Pranayama are interconnected. There are also internal and external martial arts systems, which practice forms of pranayama. Yet, most martial arts can track their lineage back to Yoga. The science of pranayama has evolved over thousands of years.

Pranayama is the fourth limb of Patanjali's Yoga. Within the past few centuries, pranayama has become globally popular, due to its healing properties. The Hatha Yoga Pradipika is believed to have been written in the 15th century. The Gheranda-Samhita is said to have been written in the late 17th century. Both of the above-mentioned texts give details concerning a variety of pranayama techniques for healing.

Within the Hatha Yoga Pradipika, instructions are given for Surya Bhedan, Ujjayi, Sitkari, Sitali, Bhastrika, Bhramari, Murchha, and Plavini. Kapalabhati is covered just a little earlier, in the Hatha Yoga Pradipika, under the instructions for the Shatkarmas. Yet, the exact origin of pranayama is still unclear.

It is said that Brahman priests developed pranayama for oral transmission of the Vedas. The Vedas are a compilation of prayers and hymns. The Vedas took shape in written form, approximately 4,000 years ago. Long before the Vedas were put in writing, Brahman priests carried the message in their minds.

Considering the size of the Vedas, to recite them from memory, requires a sharp mind and amazing breath control. To this day, pranayama is still practiced during pooja, and while reciting the Vedas. Prayers and hymns are found in every religion. Therefore, anyone, of any religion, could practice pranayama, while saying their daily prayers for deeply spiritual inspiration.

Outside of India, pranayama is not often practiced during prayer. Pranayama's value for stress reduction, general health, and asana practice, are well known. Many different types of athletes practice pranayama to enhance their physical performance. Expectant mothers practice pranayama in natural child birth and prenatal classes.

Regulation of breath control has many different purposes. Any time is a good time to control one's breath. No matter how many times we practice breath awareness, one stressful situation can cause us to lose control of our breathing. When we have no control over our breathing, our blood pressure may also follow suit. When breath is out of control, the mind will also be out of balance.

The practice of pranayama is a time-tested method, which continues to progress as we record changes and results. Yoga teachers would do a great service, to future generations, by recording notes regarding results they have observed, due to the regular practice of pranayama techniques and other Yogic methods. For the sake of privacy, it is best not to record names, but notes create a written record of progress.

WHAT IS PRANAYAMA?

As we become more familiar with yoga and the Indian tradition of the 8 limbs of Hatha yoga, we are likely to hear of Pranayama or yoga breathing and practice some of the techniques in this limb of yoga. While some styles of yoga encourage the combination of asana and Pranayama (primarily ujjayi breathing), Pranayama is a separate limb of yoga and is usually practiced separately to yoga asana.

Pranayama is comprised of the root words "Prana" meaning breath or life force, "yama" meaning control or discipline and "ayam" which means expansion. Translations of the meaning of pranayama include "expansion of the life force through breath control". In practical terms it refers to a set of breathing techniques that are used for relaxation, concentration and meditation.

In a similar manner to the development of yoga asana, these breathing techniques have been developed and expanded over the years by subsequent masters. The earliest references to Pranayama were made in the Upanishads. This reference was further clarified and refined by Patanjali in the yoga sutras, where he defined it as the 4th limb of yoga. Patenjali originally defined only 3 breathing techniques. These 3 techniques have been further expanded to the numerous techniques that exist today.

The importance of Prana is emphasized throughout yoga. Many yoga masters illustrate this by demonstrating the importance of breath for sustaining life. A very effective illustration comes by comparing the time people can survive without food (a few weeks), water (a few days) with the amount of time one could survive without air (only a few minutes). Efficient and effective breathing is essential to take in the required amounts of oxygen in order to sustain daily activities.

Yoga identifies 4 phases to the breathing cycle, all of which should be should be controlled, these are:

•Inhalation (Puraka) - which focuses on controlling the intake of air, keeping it smooth and efficient

•Internal retention of air (antara kumbhaka) - which focuses on controlling the retention of air within the lungs after an inhalation

•Exhalation (Recaka) - which focuses on controlling the expelling of used air and waist from the lungs

•External retention (bahya kumbhaka) - which focuses on controlling the retention of empty lungs after an exhalation.

Many, but not all, Pranayama techniques focus on extending the time for each of these 4 stages of the breathing cycle. This includes developing a long, smooth and steady inhalation that lasts the same duration as the exhalation and making sure that the lungs are completely full or completely empty at the end of each. It also includes extending the length of time the breath is held with the lungs full and the lungs empty to increase the efficiency of the breathing cycle. Controlling the breath in this manner requires the use of the mind to resist the natural and automatic impulses and desires of the body to breath, particularly during the internal and external retention of the breath.

Not only do these yoga breathing techniques have a direct impact on the brain through changes to the amount of oxygen brought to the brain through the blood, but focusing on the breath in this manner has a profound effect on the mind and concentration. All of which makes Pranayama an important practice to enhance relaxation, concentration (Dharana) and meditation (Dhyana).

It is interesting and important to note that even the earliest descriptions of Pranayama included certain cautions relating to its practice and suggest following the guidance of a master. B.K.S Iyengar reiterates these cautions by referring to the fight between the mind and the body around the retention of breath. Without a stable state of mind and proper care this mental fight can lead deep mental dislocation and damage leading to a split in the personality or schizophrenia. It is unclear whether any cases have ever occurred as a result of practicing yoga breathing techniques.

On a more practical level restricting oxygen flow to the brain can lead to faintness, light-headedness or dizziness. If any of these or any other pain or adverse effects are experienced then the practice should be stopped and medical advice sought.

HOW DOES PRANAYAMA WORK?

During respiration we breathe in air, and the lungs oxygenate the blood and expel carbon dioxide and other waste gases from the blood in a process known as alveoli. Those gases are expelled when we exhale. This process is subconscious or autonomic, and is not necessarily happening in a balanced and efficient manner.

Pranayama relates to bringing mental consciousness to the normally subconscious activity of breathing in order to make it more efficient and balance the oxygen, carbon dioxide and other soluble gas levels in the blood. Through this consciousness we are using the mind to control the body. In yogic terms being able to control the mind is essential in for concentration (Dharana) and meditation (Dhyana). In practical term greater mental control helps to bring emotional control and balance and mental clarity.

In addition to this pranayama aims to improve the efficiency of oxygenation of the blood. On average people tend to take short shallow breaths, a situation which is exaggerated when stressed or emotional. During this shallow breathing it is estimated that the average person uses only between half and two thirds of their lung capacity, with the remaining healthy lung surface remaining unused. This means that by breathing more optimally each breath can transfer up to fifty percent more oxygen into the blood to feed the body.

When we breathe not all of the inhaled air is exhaled. Some of air inhaled and waste carbon dioxide remains in the lungs and windpipe during exhalation when inefficient, shallow breathing is used. This continues to recycle in the respiratory system reducing the amount of new oxygen available for alveoli. By breathing deeply and completely emptying the lungs, far less of this stale air and carbon dioxide remains in the lungs improving the effectiveness of each breath.

RULES TO PRACTICE PRANAYAMA OR YOGA

- Start to practice not before the age of eight to ten years.

- Yoga exercise is equally useful for both sexes: male and female.

- Always practice in a peaceful, clam, noiseless and airy environment.

- Wear clothes which are sufficient to protect the body.

- Avoid wearing tight clothes.

- Practice on empty stomach, two hours after breakfast and four hours after a meal, and an hour after having a cup of tea or coffee

- Start practicing for short periods and gradually increase the duration.

- The practitioner should be a vegetarian as far as possible.

USEFUL TIPS FOR PRACTICING YOGA

- Warming up exercise is essential before yoga practice for slimming, shaping figure and obtaining perfect results.

- Brisk walk in the fresh morning air is very beneficial and gives exercise to the whole body, especially useful for hips and thighs.

- Always cool down after a yoga session. You begin to feel more poised, loose limned, coordinated, stretched and toned, feel as if you are gliding rather than walking.

- If you are overweight do not run. Remember, weight - bearing exercises strain your joints even more.

- Pre - exercise meal should be light.

- Cool down after exercising a session with slow and gentle stretches.

- Consult a doctor or a yoga teacher before embarking on any yogic exercise program, especially when you are above 45 years of age, pregnant, have a personal or family history of high blood pressure or heart problem.

- Too much and too fast yogic practice does not provide instant results: these simply lead to injuries, aches and pains.

What are the benefits of Pranayama?

At the anatomical level these specific breathing techniques aim to improve the strength of the diaphragm and the capacity of the lungs to improve the efficiency of the respiratory system, helping to increase fitness and increase the amount of oxygen entering the blood stream per breath. This oxygen helps to provide essential energy for muscle and brain function.

On a more detailed level pranayama is thought to:

•Increase concentration, creativity and cognitive brain functions

•Increase relaxation and calmness by releasing tension

•Improved mind and physical control, helping control emotions and relieve tension.

•Improved signing through increases abdominal and diaphragm strength and control

Yoga breathing is also thought to help with the many medical conditions, with clinical trial evidence to support some of these claims. It should be noted that pranayama should be a compliment to current treatments and should be practiced under the guidance of an experienced yoga master.

Specific conditions that respond to improved breath control include:

•Asthma,

•Allergies,

•High or low blood pressure,

•Stress-related heart conditions,

•Hyperactivity,

•Insomnia,

Chapter 9: Benefits Of Pranayama - The Yoga Of Breath

Within Patanjali's Yoga Sutra, we learn the fourth limb of Raja Yoga is pranayama. This places a high value on what some people refer to as "breathing." Yet, pranayama is actually the systematic cultivation of prana (energy). When one practices pranayama, the ratio of breath is important for controlling the amount of energy one draws in.

The specific pranayama technique that is practiced can bring about a variety of different benefits, which improve the quality of life. The many different benefits of pranayama, which is the energy control (Yogic breathing) practiced in all forms of Yoga, could consume a small book. Those, who practice Yoga regularly, are able to appreciate these benefits to the fullest. Pranayama benefits the mind and physical body in many ways.

Pranayama and Lowered Breath Rate for Longevity

Since breathing is very controlled, in all styles of Yoga, a student learns to control his or her breath rate, which slows from an average of 15 breaths per minute to about 5 breaths per minute, or less. This reduces one's overall breathing rate by about one third. Within some circles of Yogic philosophy, it is believed that your life expectancy depends on the amount of breaths you take in the course of life. Therefore, the slower you breathe, the longer you will live.

Pranayama for Emotional Health

This decreased breath rate leads to a lower heart rate, lower blood pressure, healthier internal organs, a relaxed body, and states of euphoria. What a trade off - and breathing is free. In fact, pranayama for drug rehabilitation is well worth a deeper study and research. Even if it does not always work, pranayama is much less expensive than standard drug rehabilitation methods; and when practiced correctly, it has no bad side effects.

Pranayama for Heart Health

Pranayama practice promotes better blood circulation. As you take in deep, controlled breaths, more oxygen enters your lungs and is transported through the blood stream to every cell in your body. Through better blood circulation, your heart health will also improve. The heart is the hardest working of our vital organs. By some estimates, the heart beats approximately 100,000 times per day. The amount of oxygen reaching your heart is crucial in prolonging life and maintaining a healthy heart.

Pranayama improves the functions of body organs. The digestive system improves and the chances of a digestive system-related disease decreases through the practice of pranayama. The fact is: We need a certain amount of air within the digestive system to maintain a steady flow. Pranayama decreases fatigue which will improve your mood, make you feel more energized, and your immune system is also strengthened. Due to the fact pranayama requires deep controlled breaths where you are taking in large amounts of oxygen; your internal organs are getting the appropriate amount of oxygen to function properly. This much needed oxygen helps to remove toxins from the body, which aids in the prevention of diseases.

Pranayama for Mental Health

Pranayama improves mental health. The breathing techniques require that you free your mind of negative thoughts. As you free your mind through breathing, you will alleviate stress. Pranayama prepares your mind for meditation. It will help you gain control over your mind. You will experience a feeling of inner peace and more restful sleep.

Pranayama for Holistic Health

Pranayama improves your memory and concentration levels. As we grow older, lung capacity naturally decreases. Pranayama can improve lung function as we age. It can decrease, and even reverse, some of the effects of old age - such as loss of vitality, joint pain, stiffening muscles, less flexible joints, rheumatism, headaches, backaches, sluggish diaphragm, and hardening of the arteries, which leads to poor circulation.

PRACTICES OF PRANAYAMA

You can easily and quickly control and develop body, mind and soul through breath control or the control of prana. By controlling the act of breathing you can efficiently control all the various motions in the body and the different nerve currents that are running through the body. Thus in the practices of pranayama we find many varieties of exercises, to suit the different constitutions and temperaments of the practitioners, and also their different purposes. Some of these, namely ujjayi and plavini, are outlined below, beginning with the most simple of techniques, pranayama while walking, and pranayama while lying down.

Pranayama while walking

Walk with the head up, shoulders back and with chest expanded. Inhale slowly through both nostrils counting Aum mentally three times, one count for each step. Then retain the breath while you count 12 Aums. Then exhale slowly through both nostrils while you count six Aums. Take a respiratory pause or rest after one pranayama counting 12 Aums. If you find it difficult to count Aum with each step, count Aum without having any concern with the steps.

Kapalbhati can also be done during walking. Those who are very busy can practice during their morning and evening walks. It is like killing two birds with one stone. You will find it very pleasant to practice pranayama while walking in an open space, when a delightful gentle breeze is blowing. You will be invigorated and innervated quickly and to a considerable degree. Practice, feel and realize the marked, beneficial influence of this kind of pranayama. Those who walk briskly, repeating Aum mentally or verbally, practice this natural pranayama without any effort.

Pranayama while lying down

•Lie down on your back on a blanket, quite at ease. Keep the hands on the ground by your sides and your legs straight. The heels should be kept together, but the toes can remain a little apart. Relax all the muscles and the nerves. Those who are very weak can practice pranayama in this pose while lying on the ground or on their bed.

•Draw the breath slowly inside through both nostrils, without making any noise. Retain the breath as long as you can do so with comfort. Then exhale slowly through both nostrils. Repeat the process 12 times in the morning and 12 times in the evening.

•Chant Aum mentally during the practice. If you like you can also practice in sukhasana, an easy comfortable sitting posture.

•This is a combined exercise of asana, pranayama, meditation and rest. It gives rest not only to the body but also to the mind. It provides relief, comfort and ease. This is very suitable for aged people.

Alternate nostril breathing

•Sit in padmasana. Close your eyes. Concentrate on trikuti, the space between the two eyebrows. Close the right nostril with your right thumb. Inhale slowly through the left nostril as long as you can do it with comfort. Then exhale very, very slowly through the same nostril. Do it 12 times. This is one round.

•Then inhale through the right nostril by closing the left nostril with your right ring and little fingers and exhale very slowly through the same nostril. Do it 12 times. This is one round.

•Do not make any sound during inhalation and exhalation. Mentally repeat your ishta mantra during the practice. In the second week of practice, do two rounds, in the third week, three rounds. Take a rest for two minutes when one round is over. If you take a few normal breaths, when one round is over, that will give you sufficient rest and you will be fresh for the next round. There is no kumbhaka in this exercise. You can increase the number of rounds according to your strength and capacity.

Sukha purvaka (easy comfortable) pranayama

Sit in padmasana or siddhasana in your meditation room, before the picture of your ishta devata, guiding deity. Close the right nostril with the right thumb and inhale very, very slowly through the left nostril. Then close the left nostril also with your little and ring fingers of the right hand. Retain the breath as long as comfortable. Then exhale very, very slowly through the nostril after releasing the thumb. Now half the process is over. Then draw air through the right nostril. Retain the air as before and exhale it very, very slowly through the left nostril.

All these six processes constitute one pranayama. Do 20 in the morning and 20 in the evening and gradually increase the number. Have the bhava, mental attitude that all the daivi sampat, divine qualities such as mercy, love, forgiveness, shanti, joy, etc. are entering into your system along with the inhalation. As you breathe out, feel all the asuri sampat, devilish qualities, such as lust, anger, greed, etc. are being thrown out. Repeat Aum or Gayatri mentally during pooraka, kumbhaka and rechaka.

This pranayama removes all diseases, purifies the nadis, steadies the mind in concentration, increases the digestive fire and appetite, helps to maintain brahmacharya and awakens the kundalini that is sleeping at the mooladhara chakra.

Pranava pranayama

The three processes of pranayama — expiration, inspiration and retention — each correspond to a letter of the Sanskrit alphabet forming the mantra Aum.

Sitting in padmasana, meditate on the tip of the nose, visualizing the Devi as Gayatri, a girl of red complexion, surrounded by numberless rays like the image of the moon, mounted on a swan, hamsa, and holding a mace in her hand. She is the visible symbol of the Sanskrit letter 'A'. The Sanskrit letter 'U' has as its visible symbol Savitri, a young lady of white complexion holding a disc in her hand, riding on an eagle, garuda. The Sanskrit letter 'M' has its visible symbol Saraswati, an aged woman of black complexion, riding on a bull, holding a trident in her hand.

The aspirant should meditate that the single letter, the supreme light – the pranava Aum is the origin or source of these letters and, drawing up the air through ida nadi and the left nostril for the space of 16 matras, meditate on the syllable A. Then, retaining the inspired air for the space of 64 matras, one should meditate on the syllable U. The aspirant should then exhale for the space of 32 matras, meditating on the syllable M.

One should practice thus in the above order again and again.

General Notes for the Pranayama Practice

There are innumerable rules and regulations pertaining to pranayama. The main points are to exercise moderation, balance and common sense, with regard to inner and outer thinking and living. However, for those who seriously wish to take up the advanced practices of pranayama, the guidance of a guru or experienced teacher is essential.

•Breathing: Always breathe through the nose, not the mouth unless specifically instructed otherwise. The nose should be cleaned regularly by jala neti prior to the practice session. Be aware of the nostrils throughout the techniques. While inhaling the nostrils should dilate or expand outwards. And while exhaling they should relax back to their normal position.

•Time of Practice: The best time to practice pranayama is during the early morning. The body is fresh and the mind has very few irritants. However, if this is not a good time just after sunset, tranquilizing pranayamas may be performed before sleep. Try to practice regularly at the same time and place each day.

•Regularity in practice increases strength and willpower, as well as acclimates the body and mind to the increased panic force. Do not be in a hurry. Slow, steady progress is essential.

•Place of Practice: Practice in a quiet, clean and pleasant room which is well ventilated, but not draughty. Generally, avoid practicing in direct sunlight as the body will become over- heated, except at dawn when the soft rays of the early morning sun are beneficial.

•Practicing in a draught or wind, in air-conditioning or under a fan may upset the body temperature and cause mills.

•Sitting Position: A comfortable, sustainable meditation posture is necessary to enable efficient breathing and body steadiness during the practice. The body should be as relaxed as possible throughout the practice, with the spine, neck and head centered. Sit on a folded blanket or cloth of natural fiber to ensure the maximum condition of energy during the practice.

•Clothes: Loose, comfortable clothing made of natural fibers should be worn during the practice. The body may be covered with a sheet or blanket when it is cold, or to keep insects away.

•Empty Stomach: Wait at least three to four hours after meals before starting pranayama. Food in the stomach puts pressure on the diaphragm and lungs, making full, deep respiration difficult.

•Diet: A balanced diet of protein, carbohydrates, fats, vitamins and minerals is suitable for most pranayama practices. A combination of grains, fresh fruit and vegetables with little milk product (almond milk is an alternative choice).

Chapter 10: Pranayama For Beginners

Pranayama is the fourth limb of Astanga yoga, and is also called as the "Heart of Yoga." Pranayama teaches us to how to use our lungs to the optimum capacity; as a result of which, the cells in our body are able to get sufficient quantity of oxygen. Though there are about 20 pranayamas; some of the pranayamas which are easy, and can easily be practiced by beginners are as follows Sunhat pranayama, Pranava pranayama, Kapalabhati, Anuloma Viloma pranayama, Bhramari pranayama and Sheetkari pranayama.

SUKHA PRANAYAMA:

This is the easiest of all the pranayamas. This is also called as deep abdominal breathing. Sukha pranayama is a great stress buster and a powerful mental tonic. It's a great pranayama for relieving stress, fear, worry, anxiety and depression.

Technique:

Sit down comfortably in a cross-legged posture, with your back straight, and chin parallel to the ground. Gently close your eyes now. All you need to do here is to concentrate on your breath and the movement your abdomen; breathe-in to the count of 5 and breathe-out to the count of 5. Keep your one hand over your abdomen so that you can feel the expansion and contraction as you inhale and exhale. As you breathe-in, your abdomen slowly expands and as you breathe out your abdomen contracts. Do this pranayama for about 3 to 5 minutes; after don't a couple of rounds of this pranayama, you shall feel quite peaceful and elated.

ANULOMA VILOMA PRANAYAMA:

This is also called as the alternate Norstril Breathing. Anuloma Viloma is beneficial in the treatment of various diseases including heart problems, high blood pressure, and blockages in the arteries, insomnia, panic disorders, and depression.

Technique:

Sit in a cross-legged posture with your back straight and chin parallel to the ground; gently close your eyes now. Make an Apana mudra with your right hand (join the tip of the middle finger, ring finger, and the thumb together; the other two fingers should be pointed outwards). Now close your right nostril with the help of your thumb, and exhale out all your breath from the left nostril; your abdomen should sink all the way in. This is the starting position of this pranayama. Inhale from the left nostril to the count of 4; your abdomen expands outwards. Next, close your left nostril with the help of the ring finger and middle finger, and exhale through the right nostril to the count of 8; your abdomen contracts as you exhale. Now inhale from the right nostril to the count 4(your abdomen expands); close your right nostril with the thumb, and exhale through the left nostril to the count of 8(your abdomen contracts). This completes your one round of Anuloma Viloma pranayama. Do at least 15 to 20 rounds of Anuloma Viloma pranayama.

How to Start Pranayama?

Are you a person who is keen to start Pranayama but do not know how to start? People of any age, any country can easily adopt Pranayama and take the first step to stay away from majority of lifestyle diseases.

Yoga Breathing. You can live without food and water for a few days, but you cannot live without breathing for a minute. As per yoga philosophy prana is life. Prana is the Sanskrit word for breath. If you can control your breath, you can control your life. Pranayama is ideal for improving your blood circulation, improving concentration and provides a remarkable peace of mind. Pranayama practice provides you enough energy to last for the day.

Try to learn the breathing techniques of Pranayama from a yoga expert. In case you do not have access to a yoga expert, learn more about Pranayama by reading a book, seeing a video or surfing through a good website about yoga. Explore the net for yoga experts who can provide guidance on how to start Pranayama.

You have to find out the Pranayama exercises suitable for you. Pranayama exercises for you will depend on your age and present health. Alom Vilom and Kapalabhati are the most popular ones with beginners. It is recommended to start with Rhythmic Breathing and Alom Vilom for 15 to 30 minutes daily. After a week of practice, attempt other Pranayama also.

Unlike Yoga asanas, Pranayama does not have stringent flexibility requirements. Even inflexible people can do all the Pranayama exercises. Very weak people can do Alom Vilom and Rhythmic Breathing practices lying down on the floor.

Pranayama is better done outdoors. In an open park, you can do Pranayama sitting comfortably on ground or sitting on a bench. However, you can also practice Pranayama sitting in a well ventilated room where there is plenty of fresh air. Busy people can spare some time in office and do Pranayama sitting on a chair.

You can start with the following Pranayama exercises:

Rhythmic Deep Breathing.

It is the most beneficial Pranayama which can be integrated with your way of life. Rhythmic breathing can even be done walking, sitting in office or waiting at airports. It involves deepening your breath and reduce your breathing rate to 6 to 8 breaths per minute (average person breathes 15 times per minute). Less breathing rate reduces wear and tear of body while at the same time; deep breathing increases the amount of oxygen you breathe. You can recollect that before commencing a difficult task, we generally take a couple of deep breaths.

Alom Vilom.

It is the simplest Pranayama and any person can do it. Even very old or weak people can do it by lying down if they are not able to sit comfortably. Alom Vilom improves blood circulation and exercises the heart.

Kapalabhati Pranayama.

It benefits blood circulation, respiratory system, concentration and memory. Kapalabhati Pranayama is prohibited for heart patients and people with high blood pressure.

Chandra Bhedi Pranayama.

This Pranayama cools your body and lower blood pressure. If you have low blood pressure does not attempt this. Do not do this Pranayama in winter season.

Surya Bhedi Pranayama.

It provides warmth to body. If you have high blood pressure do not attempt this. Do not practice this Pranayama in summer season.

Bhramri Pranayama.

Bhramri Pranayama increases power of concentration and makes your voice melodious.

Pranayama practice for 30 minutes a day can show appreciable results in two to three weeks. To enjoy the benefits of Pranayama, do not procrastinate, start yoga breathing now.

THE ART OF PRANAYAMA BREATHING PROCESS - THE VARIOUS STAGES

The ancient yogis developed the breathing exercises of nadi shodhana, shitali, kapalabhati, viloma, and ujjayi. It takes some time before you can start observing the benefits of these exercises on your body. Pranayama comes with various difficulty levels and to practice correctly, you need to initially train under a yoga expert. Practicing these exercises in a wrong way can lead to diseases, related to the lungs.

Pranayama exercises work by refining or tuning the following 4 breathing stages:

a) Puraka - the stage of inhalation or oxygen intake

b) Abhyantara kumbhaka - the pause before exhalation or discharge of carbon dioxide

c) Rechaka - the stage of exhalation

d) Bahya kumbhaka - the pause after exhalation

Refining the Breathing Stages through Pranayama

A fast-paced life, full of stress, results in improper execution of the 4 basic breathing stages. The people practicing yoga are able to control their breath for long intervals of time. They achieve it through regular practice of the following levels of pranayama:

a) Adhama - Essentially, you start with adhama as a beginner. You execute puraka for 12 seconds, followed by execution of kumbhaka for 48 seconds, and of rechaka for 24 seconds.

The ratio of puraka, kumbhaka, and rechaka should stay as 1:4:2 for all levels of pranayama.

b) Madhyama - Perfecting adhama, you proceed to madhyama by executing puraka for 24 seconds, followed by execution of kumbhaka for 96 seconds, and of rechaka for 48 seconds.

c) Uttama - Having perfected madhyama, you move on to the advanced stage of pranayama, also called "Uttama". Here, you execute puraka for 32 seconds, followed by extended kumbhaka for 128 seconds, and extended rechaka for 64 seconds.

Once you master the art of uttama, you can achieve the state of keval kumbhaka. It implies arresting and resting breath for fairly long intervals of time, at will. In this state, the body is rid of all types of diseases.

THE FOUR GENERAL RULES FOR DOING PRANAYAMA

Pranayama or the practice of restraining the prana or breath is one of the key components of yoga and is being taught freely to students who are paying for yoga classes.

However, for us who are at the conservative end of the yoga practitioners' spectrum, pranayama is not something that we teach freely. We know that pranayama is a powerful practice that when practiced wrongly, could do harm to the person doing it and the people around him or her.

This is because pranayama has four general rules:

1. Only a moralist should practice it

By "moralist", we mean a person who is moving in the direction of self-development and service to others. Any responsible teacher of yoga should make sure that the student is not a selfish person. A selfish mind is strengthened by pranayama; it does not make it less selfish. Similarly, a person who is kind to others will become strong in that trait.

2. One should adhere to a strict vegetarian diet

The second rule is that the student should be a strict vegetarian. Certain foods, stimulants and addictive substances activate the body's glands and nervous system, causing undesirable behavior and emotion in a person. With pranayama, these behaviors become expressed more strongly, even if it against the person's conscience.

3. Fix the mind to one point

During inhalation and exhalation, the mind should be fixed to one point. This rule has been especially emphasized for the last 3500 years. During pranayama, different things will disturb your practice. These include your emotions, your memories to your mental tendencies. If you don't fix your mind on one point like, for example, the tip of your nose, these will disturb your concentration, which is an important factor in doing pranayama.

4. Recite a mantra while doing pranayama

You should recite a mantra with each inhalation and exhalation, while at the same time concentrating your mind on one point.

This is why the tip of your nose is the best point to fix your mind.

When you're doing pranayama, you're not only breathing air, you are also breathing vitality. That vitality is not your own vital energy, but it is the vital energy of the Universal Consciousness which controls you. The link between the mind, prana and Universal Consciousness is the mantra.

As you can see the practice of pranayama is a very precise science. These aspects should not be omitted by the yoga teacher, but unfortunately, they are omitted in commercial yoga. Usually yoga teachers do not know enough about the psycho-physical and psycho-spiritual aspects of pranayama to know how to teach it properly. And thus negative effects are seen: headaches, nose bleeds, high blood pressure or strong uncontrollable emotions.

PRANAYAMA EXERCISES

As you all know, oxygen is the supreme necessity for our bodies and without it we cannot survive perhaps even for a couple of minutes. There is almost unlimited oxygen all around us. But we do not know how to get its benefits fully as we never utilize our full lung capacity. Consequently our body is sort of starved of oxygen. Pranayama is a technique to govern the breathing process. Breathing is normally an unconscious process. Through Pranayama, a person learns to consciously govern the breath to bring harmony into the body, mind and spirit. Regular breathing exercises tremendously increase the capacity to inhale and absorb life-giving oxygen. The capacity of the lungs even during unconscious breathing increases. There are four breathing exercises which are particularly helpful:

1) BHASTRIKA PRANAYAMA: In this you repeatedly breathe in to the full capacity of your lungs and then breathe out completely. Should be done for minimum 2 minutes; maximum is 5 minutes

Helps heart, lungs, brain, nervous system, and in migraine, depression, paralysis, etc.

2) KAPALBHATI PRANAYAMA: In this breathing exercise, you exhale completely and with force while pulling in your abdomen. Inhaling is done automatically and in a normal manner. Should be repeated 30 times, maximum 10 minutes.

Helps in diabetes, constipation, gastric problems, hepatitis B, obesity, cholesterol, asthma, snoring and even in cancer and AIDS.

3) ANULOMA VILOMA PRANAYAMA: This pranayama is slightly more complicated but the benefits are enormous.

(a) Close your right nasal orifice with your thumb and breathe in deeply with your left nose.

(b) Now open the right nose, close the left nose with middle and ring fingers, and breathe out completely with your right nose.

(c) Next, breathe in deeply with the right nose, close the right nose with your thumb, and breathe out completely with the left nose.

Start again with (a), then move onto (b) then (c).

Repeat for at least 10 minutes.

Helps in heart, high blood pressure, heart blockages, arthritis, migraine, depression, neural system, paralysis, asthma, sinus, allergy, Parkinson's disease, etc

4) BHRAMARI PRANAYAMA: Here you close your ears with thumbs; keep index fingers on your forehead and remaining three fingers should cover both eyes. Breathe in deeply and then breathe out through the nose while making a humming sound like a honey bee. Should be done seven to ten times.

Helps in cases of tension, hypertension, high blood pressure, heart, heart blockages, paralysis, migraine pain, etc. Improves concentration and confidence.

Now let us summarize the benefits that accrue if a person does Pranayama every morning (or evening) for a period of 20 to 25 minutes :

-It increases lung capacity and improves breathing efficiency,

-It improves circulation, helps normalize blood pressure and improves cardiovascular efficiency,

-It boosts the immune system and enhances immunity,

-It increases energy levels and gives lots of positive energy,

-It strengthens and tones the nervous system,

-It combats anxiety and depression and improves sleep,

-It improves digestion and excretory functions,

-It provides massage to the internal organs, stimulates the glands and enhances endocrine functions,

-It normalizes body weight and provides great conditioning for weight loss,

- And lastly it improves skin tone and complexion

Chapter 11: Importance Of Bhastrika And Kapalbhati Pranayama

Bhastrika and kapalbhati pranayama are both Yoga breathing exercises that can help the practitioner improve lung capacity and manage breathing conditions such as asthma. These breathing exercises are best used in the morning and both provide benefits that impact the entire body, resulting in more energy and better overall health.

Kapalbhati pranayama helps the internal organs to work better by exercising and massaging the chest and abdomen. Kapalbhati increases lung capacity because it allows the practitioner to inhale more fresh oxygen and to exhale more carbon dioxide, helping to cleanse the body of harmful toxins. This type of breathing exercise benefits the respiratory system and is especially helpful when a practitioner is suffering from diseases and conditions that affect breathing, such as a cold, bronchitis, rhinitis, sinusitis, deviated septum and even more serious conditions such as tuberculosis and emphysema.

Additionally, kapalbhati is beneficial to the digestive system, helping the practitioner to improve digestion and to ease the effects of indigestion, constipation and gastritis. Since kapalbhati increases circulation, heart rate and the amount of red blood cells in the blood, it allows the practitioner to become more energetic. This is particular beneficial to overweight practitioners who find more energy and find themselves less exhausted as they move about their day. It also stabilizes the glands of the endocrine system, which affects the entire body and even assists with the nervous system through the constant cleansing of brain cells as a result of the increased level of oxygen in the blood. Mental health is also positively affected and the practitioner experiences a type of bliss and relaxation after this practice.

Bhastrika pranayama is very similar in the benefits it provides the practitioner. Bhastrika is particularly beneficial to practitioners dealing with respiratory illnesses and conditions, as its forceful breathing methods help to cure conditions such as the common cold, sinus infections and the flu. It can even help to improve asthma. It can also help with the healing of conditions that affect the thyroid gland and throat problems such as those that affect the tonsils.

Regular practice of bhastrika pranayama results in younger-looking, glowing, healthy skin. Overall health is improved by most practitioners since they are able to detoxify their body by expelling the toxins as they breathe out. Increased lung capacity leads to more oxygen in the blood, which leads to more vitality.

Chapter 12: Yoga Breathing Exercises Or Pranayama For Freeing The Mind

Yoga is not to be thought of as just a series of awkward movements useful for making your body subtle and flexible. While yoga will achieve this, its benefits are much more profound. The various elements of yoga are all fundamental and without them yoga postures become simply physical movement. These elements; asanas, breathing, gaze and meditation when performed correctly will allow to become one with yourself and providing a level of awareness never before experienced.

Today we are going to take a look into pranayama, the art of breathing and breath control. With pranayama we are conscious of our breath travelling though our lungs. While this exercise that we are going to discuss is a little difficult to master, your efforts will be well worth it. Believe me.

Ujjayi breath control

This specific exercise is performed by making a soft, yet audible, sound in the back of your throat while inhaling and exhaling through the nose. In this breathing practice, you will be breathing deeply while restricting the back of throat allowing the air to swirl in the back of the throat so as to create a low humming sound. The sound should resemble that of wind in the trees or ocean waves. Some people have also said this sound resembles the famous dark villan of Star Wars: Darth Vader, however I don't think he was practicing pranayama. Follow the humming sound as it will help you concentrate on the synchronization of breath.

Some of you may find it difficult to produce the humming sound, but there is a simple exercise to help you. Try sitting upright and deeply inhale through the nose and then exhale through the mouth, however, while exhaling make the back of your throat vibrate and hum or purr as if you were whispering. You should be able to feel the air passing through your throat. Breathe like this several times then midway through exhaling close your mouth and exhale through your nose.

The second part is also tricky to perform correctly. While inhaling through the nose you should try to replicate the same swirling sound in your throat. As with all new things, with practice you will be able to do this automatically without effort.

With this breathing exercise we must be totally relaxed, this may seem odd but you should also keep your face muscles relaxed during the exercise. Your chest shouldn't heave and your collar bone should only slightly raise and fall.

We are trying to create a smooth rhythm in our breath throughout this pranayama. Learn to listen to the breath in order to achieve the best results.

THE CORRECT POSITION FOR PRANAYAMA

What is the correct position for performing this pranayama exercise? There isn't one. It can be performed either sitting or lying down.

In this article I want to talk about the lying position as I think this enables a greater level of relaxation. We will need some props for this (yoga blocks, folded blankets, thick books, etc.) as your chest, neck and head must be raised from the floor. Your back should be gently arched with your thighs and backside on the floor while your upper back should be supported to just below the same height as the tops of your thighs (8-10 inches), your neck and head should also be comfortably supported. It is important that your head is not inclined backwards, but slightly higher than your neck. It is also a good idea to cover your eyes and ears.

>Relax your throat and your entire body; try to focus on an imaginary point inside your chest. Gently close your eyes and look downwards towards the imaginary point, this will help you relax. If your eyes are looking upwards your mind will become full of invasive thoughts. The next step is to breath normally, becoming acquainted with this

position and your body. Fully expand your chest but do not tense your diaphragm.

The next step is to inhale normally but exhale deeply and slowly releasing all of the air from your lungs, feel it leave your body. You should try to synchronize as much as possible the movements of your abdomen and diaphragm and keep the flow of your breathing stable at all times. Do this for about 15 cycles.

The next phase is the exact contrary of the previous one. Here we are inhaling deeply but exhaling normally without effort. You should experience your breath rising from your lower chest to your throat, be conscious of this. Once again 15 cycles.

Finally, you will be breathing in and out deeply and peacefully in a controlled manner, completely filling your lungs with air and then totally emptying your lungs. End the exercise by exhaling. One again 15 cycles is sufficient.

After you have finished, gently sit up from the supports under your back and head, remove them, then lay on the floor in a Savasana posture "the corpse" and relax for 3-5 minutes.

If it is too difficult to perform the humming sound in your throat, just practice the breathing exercise without the sound. You can always practice later.

PRANAYAMA BREATHING TECHNIQUES

Pranayama is a series of ancient breathing techniques that originated in India over 2,000 years ago. These techniques have a wide variety of benefits. They can increase longevity, eliminate depression and help to regulate the various systems of your body. Pranayama is often taught as part of yoga classes. Many of the poses in yoga, known as asanas, are most effectively performed while using pranayama breathing techniques. Inhaling and exhaling in the specific manner prescribed by these techniques makes the lungs stronger and brings the nervous system into balance. If you are a yoga instructor thinking about teaching pranayama breathing techniques, here are a few of the most important ones you should focus on:

1. SURYABHEDAN

- Sit in a comfortable position.

- Use your right hand's middle and index fingers to close your left nostril.

- Breathe in slowly through the right side.

- Use the thumb on your right hand to stop air flow on the right.

- Breath out through the left side.

Benefits

- Slows down the aging process

- Purifies the blood

- Digestion is improved

- Energy and body heat are increased

2. CHANDRABHEDAN

- Sit in a position conducive to meditating.

- Your shoulders should be relaxed and your back should remain straight.

- The right nostril should be closed using the thumb from the right hand.

- Breathe in through the left side of your nose.

- Using the middle and index fingers of the right hand, close the left.

- Breathe out through the right.

Benefits

- This technique has been known to cure heartburn and cool the body.

3. BHASTRIKA

- A meditative position is preferable for this technique.

- You should relax the muscles in the shoulders. The back should be kept straight.

- The right thumb should be used to close the right nostril. As you do this, the right elbow should be at the same level as the right shoulder.

- With your eyes closed, begin to slowly breathe in and out through the left opening in your nose. Gradually increase your breathing.

- After repeating these steps 20 times, inhale deeply and hold it in for as long as you can.

- You can now close the left side breathe through the right side and repeat the process.

Benefits

- The blood is purified

- Digestion is improved

- Toxins are eliminated from the body

- The nervous system is regulated

- Excess fat is eliminated

4. ANULOM-VILOM

- Sit in a relaxed and balanced position.

- Close the right nostril with the thumb on your right hand.

- Breathe in through the left opening in your nose.

- Using the middle and index fingers on the right hand, close the left side.

- Breathe out and in through the right opening.

- With the thumb on your right hand, close the right side.

- Breathe out through the left.

Benefits

- Increases longevity

- Body temperature becomes balanced

- Circulation of blood is improved

- Stress is eliminated

5. UJJAYI

- Sit erect so you feel comfortable.

- Using both nostrils, breathe in deeply and slowly.

- Hold your breath as long as you can.

- As you breathe out, contract your air passage to create a whispering sound.

Benefits

- Keeps the throat, chest and lungs healthy

- Blood circulation is improved

- The thyroid gland is stimulated

- The vocal cord is made stronger

9 781778 065231